TOTAL AWARENESS

A Woman's Safety Book

DARREN & BETH LAUR

Sono Nis Press

VICTORIA BC CANADA

Canadian Cataloguing in Publication Data

Laur, Darren, 1965-
    Total awareness

    ISBN 1-55039-098-8

    1. Women—Crimes against—Prevention. I. Laur, Beth, 1968- II.
Title.
HV6250.4.W65L38 1999   613.6'6'082   C99-910382-2

COVER DESIGN: Jim Brennan
TEXT DESIGN: Jim Bennett

Published by
SONO NIS PRESS
PO Box 5550, Station B
Victoria, BC V8R 6S4 Canada
http://www.islandnet.com/~sononis/
E-mail: sononis@islandnet.com

Printed in Canada by
Friesen's

Contents

Preface

Violent behaviour, especially towards women, continues to be pervasive in our society. Concerned about this state of affairs, we started teaching self-defence classes and safety seminars in 1993, and have since reached thousands of women of all ages. This book is based on our safety seminar program for women, "Total Awareness." Through Darren's work as a police officer, our own extensive research on the topic, and feedback from our students, our understanding continues to evolve.

While we strongly encourage *all* women (regardless of age, size, physical ability, or cultural background) to take a creditable physical self-defence course, the single most critical concept we hope to impart in our teachings is the importance of *awareness*. Awareness helps prevent the crime before it happens. In this book, we present many effective and simple methods by which you can protect yourself to greatly decrease the risks of becoming a victim of crimes such as purse-snatching, home invasion, sexual assault, identity theft, and others. If you are aware of how and why a predator picks you or your property as a target, you can, in most situations, avoid becoming a victim. We also provide information on your rights under Canadian law regarding self-defence and stalking; procedures to expect if you report a sexual assault; and ways to help translate fear into a life-saving defensive response.

The reality is that today we live in an increasingly violent society in which the fear of crime and its emotional consequences is ever-present, particularly for women. Personal safety has become an issue of importance to everyone. We don't believe in frightening women about the realities of the street, to the point where they are afraid to leave their homes, but we don't believe in pulling any punches, either. "Political correctness" has no place in either our seminars or our self-defence courses. Knowledge is power—arm yourself with it, and keep yourself and your loved ones as safe as you can.

Note that although your attacker can be anyone, statistics tell us that most assaults on women are committed by men. Because of this, most of the references to attackers in this book are male gender specific.

Crime is not merely a dry statistic. In all its various forms, it has a devastating impact on real people. We don't want you to become a victim, and that is why we devote so much of our time to teaching women self-defence techniques and giving safety awareness courses. It is also why we have written *Total Awareness.* This book is for you.

Stay safe!

Darren and Beth

Acknowledgements

Additional information on many of the topics in this book is readily available in a number of excellent publications in print and on the Internet, and from a number of organizations. Our Selected Bibliography and Resources section offers you a starting point for further reading.

We thank the thousands of women who have taken our safety programs and convinced us to write a book which could be read and shared by many. A special thank you to editor Patricia Sloan, who took our thoughts and ideas and crafted them into our finished product. We also thank Heather Keenan and Dawn Loewen at Sono Nis Press, and especially publisher Diane Morriss, who strongly believed in our message of personal safety for women.

The loves in our lives are each other and our son, Brandon. The passion in our lives is sharing the message of personal safety with others. We thank each other and Brandon for the sacrifices made during the writing of this book.

CHAPTER ONE

Who Attacks and Why

Who?

Numerous scientific, psychological, and police studies have been conducted by criminologists in an attempt to identify those types of people who are most likely to be the offenders in an assault. A mass of research has accumulated documenting criminal profiles ranging from psychotic personalities to everyday people next door. Most women fear and imagine typical attackers as being a stranger jumping out of the bushes in the dark. This is not true. The unfortunate reality is that in a sexual assault, the attacker will most likely be someone you know, love, or trust. He could be an acquaintance, date, friend, spouse, co-worker. Of course, sexual attacks by strangers do occur and are vividly reported in the media, but the incidence of these is small in comparison.

In other types of assaults, such as robbery and purse-snatching, women must be alert and aware for their personal safety because a potential attacker could be anyone with a motive or opportunity.

Why?

Why would someone attack you? What possible motivation could a person have to hurt you or cause you harm, sometimes devastating physical and emotional injury? Those who lead kind and respectful lives do not generally expect to be confronted in such an abusive manner and are puzzled by the reasons for assaults. Although there are a variety of reasons why a person would decide to choose you as a target, three principal motivational factors have been identified: your *property*, your *body*, or your *life*—or a combination of these.

Your Property

Many street predators commit violent acts to obtain your property—such as money, credit cards, watches, jewellery, clothing, and vehicles. Usually these items are rapidly exchanged for drugs or alcohol, and only in rare cases used for such basic needs as food or accommodation.

Whenever you are confronted with an attacker, armed or not, who demands your property, *give your stuff up*. Throw it one way while you run the other way. However, do not throw it too far (more than a couple of metres), as you will only anger the attacker. Never hand anything over directly, because you could easily be grabbed. Things can be replaced; a life cannot. Risk of injury (or worse) to you is extreme if you attempt to resist. No possession is worth serious injury or death.

Your Body

A second motivation that an attacker may have for targeting you is to commit an assault—a physical assault, a sexual assault, or for the simple enjoyment of violence.

PHYSICAL ASSAULT

Of growing concern to law enforcement personnel and to the public is the increasing occurrence and violence of physical assaults, especially by or among teens. Although morally there is no justification for an unprovoked attack, most physical assaults result from an encounter in which someone's pride or ego has been challenged or ridiculed or even just perceived as such. An explosive environment is created when a person's peer group is looking on, making physical retaliation a matter of "saving face." If you are verbally confronted by someone, especially if that person is in a group, simply ignore the person and calmly leave the situation, whether it be walking on the street, at a party, in a school hallway. To confront an ego-based attacker will likely bring about a physical assault.

SEXUAL ASSAULT

Sexual assault is about power, control, degradation, and humiliation; it is rarely about the sexual act. Being sexually assaulted is one of the greatest fears which many women have, and for women who have survived such an encounter, it is their worst recurring nightmare. Typical sexual offenders are men who feel powerless and insecure, and who attempt to gain and affirm control over others, usually women, by a sexual attack.

ENJOYMENT OF VIOLENCE

Increasingly, acts of violence such as drive-by shootings, serial murders, home invasions, and swarmings are being committed for nothing more than pure enjoyment of violence. There is no apparent reason for these random acts of violence other than for the kicks these sick individuals get out of such senseless acts. These people are the most dangerous to deal with because they are not rational; they do not care about you or anyone else except themselves. To seriously hurt or kill you is just as easy to them as eating or sleeping.

Your Life

The last motivational factor that an attacker may have for choosing you as a target is for the purpose of killing you. Although there have been a number of well-publicized cases of women who have been reported missing and then later found to be dead, these cases are a rarity. The percentage of women in Canada who have died as a result of an attack is less than 1% of all women attacked. The majority of these fatalities result from an attack by a spouse or partner.

●   ●   ●

Regardless of the motivation or purpose for choosing you as a target, it is important to understand that the attacker has a distinct advantage in that he has already chosen when he will attack, where he will attack, and who he will attack. Unless you have a plan of action in place, you will be constantly playing catch-up or second-guessing the attacker, and most likely end up being victimized. Think of this catch phrase, the "Six Ps" of personal safety: "Proper Pre-Planning Prevents Poor Performance." Play "what if" games and devise your plan. The attacker has a plan of attack—so must you be prepared. Those people who are stuck in the "I can't believe this is happening to me" mindset do not have their action plan ready and are not prepared for reality, and are therefore easy prey for a predator.

CHAPTER TWO

Be Streetsafe

The Reality of the Street

The Thin Blue Line

Many people think that the police are the first line of defence when it comes to protecting citizens from criminals. In a perfect world, this statement would be true, but the reality is *you* are going to be the first line of defence, not the police.

Fact: Most police departments are reactive rather than proactive.

With increased call loads, personnel shortages, time spent in court, and financial restraints, police departments are necessarily becoming much more reactive to crime than actually working to prevent it.

Fact: There are more criminals than police.

There are more criminals walking the streets than ever before. The phrase "the thin blue line" originated among police, who know if the criminal element were to band together, police could do little to prevent their combined criminal acts.

Fact: Experienced criminals know how to avoid getting caught by police.

Police catch mainly inexperienced criminals. This is because the experienced criminal has learned from his mistakes. The criminal knows that the odds are in his favour to get away with a crime rather than answer for it.

Fact: Most criminals are not really afraid of the police.

Most criminals consider police an annoyance to their activities more than anything else. They understand that police are more accountable for their actions and are under heavy constraints internally, legally, and publicly, and under heavy media scrutiny. This problem is compounded by the fact that the judicial system restrains the crime-fighting capabilities of police.

Fact: Even if police do catch the criminal, the odds are he will be back on the street the next day.

It is a reality that many criminals who get caught by the police either have to be released because the Criminal Code requires it, or are released by the courts the next day.

The Courts

If police do catch the criminal, the next step is court. The Canadian criminal justice system, although one of the best in the world, still has its failings. The criminal knows that the justice system often works more for him than for the actual victim of the crime. The criminal's lawyer knows the ins and outs of the judicial jungle, and if there is a technicality that she can find for her client, she will find it.

In Canadian law, you are innocent until proven guilty. This is true even if the police catch the criminal red-handed. By going to court, not only is there is a possibility that he may get off on a technicality, but also a plea bargain may be arranged which favours the criminal. Usually accepting this plea bargain results in a lesser charge and less time served, if any time at all.

The admonition "let the punishment fit the crime" does not apply in most circumstances. It is very common for people who have committed violent crimes to be released on probation after receiving very small prison terms, of which they have served only a third. This means that if a criminal is found guilty and is sentenced to one year in jail, it is very probable that he will be released in four months. Probation conditions also often seem extremely lenient and arbitrary. For example, very recently in Victoria, a convicted serial rapist whom experts stated was at high risk to re-offend was released on a two-day unescorted pass. Such incidents often leave police (and the public) shaking their heads.

Reducing the Risk on the Street

Awareness: Your First Line of Defence

What is self-defence? When this question is asked, usual answers refer only to *physical* techniques. However, true self-defence begins long before any actual physical assault you may have to face. The first and probably the most important component in self-defence is *awareness:* awareness of yourself, your potential attacker, and your surroundings. Self-defence is a system of awareness combined with physical and mental techniques. Through awareness, many physical altercations which are commonplace on the street can be avoided.

A common strategy used by predators is to look for people who are totally oblivious to their surroundings. In fact, predators have a name for these types of people—"Vics"—meaning victims.

A recent interesting study was conducted in the United States in which investigators had a number of inmates, who were in jail for sexual assaults, watch a video of people walking around in a mall environment. During the video, each inmate was asked separately whom they thought would be easy targets. To the investigators' astonishment, each inmate picked the same people.

When asked why they picked these people as targets, the inmates stated that it appeared the people they chose were unaware of what was going on around them. Surprise is the primary tool of survival for the street predator and if you can take this tool from him, you are less likely to be chosen as a target.

We like to use the analogy of an army in time of war to explain what we mean. An army sets up perimeters as an early warning system, to counter an ambush from its enemy. The sole purpose of these early warning stations is to advise the main body of any type of aggressive act being initiated against it, to prevent being taken by a surprise attack.

Just like the army in time of war, you also need this early warning system to prevent an attack. By having this awareness mindset, you will have the insight, knowledge, and time to recognize what is going on around you and deal with any potential problems more effectively.

By being aware of your surroundings and projecting a "force presence," you send two clear messages to your potential attacker:

- I recognize that you are there, and

- To attack me may cost you physically because I'm no easy target.

This is important to understand because the street predator is a lazy animal who likes to pick easy targets. The easier the target, the better, because the risk is very small and the rewards are very great. If your demeanour suggests "I'm not a victim," the predator will more than likely leave you alone and find an easier target.

Knowing how the predator operates will go a long way in keeping you safe. Usually the predator will not attack unless he has full confidence in his ability to win the physical confrontation. This confidence comes from his ability to use surprise to his full advantage. His targets of opportunity are victims who have little awareness of their surroundings.

The predator's criminal experience comes from actual application on the street. Most street predators do not have specialized training; they have one or two techniques which they have mastered to some degree (e.g., the sucker punch and ambush are favourite tactics). This mastery has come through actual application and trial and error in real street conditions. The predator's tactics are characterized by simplicity; the simpler the better. Because of this simplicity, usually their methods are very effective.

Your Strategies—Don't Be a Target

PAY ATTENTION

Awareness of your surroundings is the key to personal safety. As mentioned, the principal strategy of the street predator is the advantage of surprise. If you are not aware of who or what is around you at all times, you become a primary target. Awareness will, in most circumstances, remove the advantage of surprise.

SCAN

Learn to be in the habit of constantly scanning your surroundings —side, front, and behind; close to you and farther away. Practice will make scanning automatic. Imagine yourself as a predator— would you choose that recessed doorway?

It is only common sense, especially when walking or cycling, to avoid dangerous situations or people. Use the middle of the road, cross the street, use another route altogether, take the bus. Rely on sounds as well as sight. What you might not be able to see, you might be able to hear—a fight around the corner, running footsteps behind you, a bicycle, motorbike, or a car approaching.

DON'T GET DISTRACTED

It is difficult, if not impossible, to be aware of your surroundings if you are distracted. Cell phones and headphones in particular lower your perception levels, and loud sounds in themselves can deaden other senses as well. If you are absorbed in window-shopping, reading a good book or magazine, or are deep in conversation, you are not fully aware. Some medications, and certainly alcohol and drugs, can impair your judgement and sensory awareness, making you a vulnerable target.

KNOW WHO'S AROUND YOU

Part of being alert to your surroundings is to be aware of the people around you, especially lone males and males in groups. When scanning, make split-second eye contact with people. By doing this, you send a message that you know the person is there. A longer eye contact or stare can be considered a challenge.

WALK STRONG AND CONFIDENT

By carrying yourself in a confident, purposeful, and self-assured manner—described as "force presence"—you immediately convey to a potential attacker that you are not a victim. A pre-occupied, aimless, lost-looking person appears to be much more vulnerable, and an easy victim is what the predator wants. It doesn't matter if you don't *feel* totally confident and strong; the important thing is to *appear* so. A self-defence course can help make you feel more powerful (see Chapter 3).

Deal with wolf whistles or harassing and intimidating comments by simply ignoring them. Confronting your attacker only places you in a potentially hostile situation, especially if the harasser is with a group of peers.

USE YOUR SIXTH SENSE

"Sixth sense", "gut instinct"—whatever you call it, your intuition is a powerful subconscious insight into situations and people. All of us, especially women, have this gift, but very few of us pay attention to it. All of us have met people for the first time and felt something funny or disturbing about them, only to find out later our instincts were correct. That is your intuition working. Learn to trust this power and use it to your full advantage. Your intuition is a million years of evolution working to keep you safe, but yet when triggered, it is often denied or trivialized. When it comes to personal safety, your intuition is a powerful tool. If you feel uneasy, there is probably a reason why, even though you cannot explain it at the time. Avoid a person or a situation which does not "feel" safe—you are probably right.

A good example of women's intuition concerns the recent arrest in Victoria of a man who videotaped women under their skirts while talking to them in his and their workplaces. *All* of the many women interviewed by police about the matter said they felt uncomfortable when they met the man. An officer involved in the investigation encouraged women: "Be aware. Trust your instincts."

KNOW WHERE YOU ARE

Always know or plan your route beforehand, especially in areas which are not familiar. A "lost" appearance indicates weakness—a sure target.

Always know where a safe place is—should it be a hotel, store, or police station—that you can reach quickly if you sense trouble. A safe place is a busy place.

If you suspect you are being followed, go to a safe place immediately. Do not go home. You do not want to show your attacker where you live. If you cannot get to a safe place, turn and confront the follower by saying loudly, "Are you following me?" and "Don't I know you?" This alerts the person that you are not only aware of his presence, thus removing the surprise tactic, but also indicates that you would be able to identify him. If the person continues to follow, run to the closest safe place, and as you are running, yell loudly for help.

If confronted and the predator wants your property, throw your belongings in one direction while you run the other to the closest safe place, yelling loudly for help.

Avoid poorly lit streets, alleys, vacant lots, and parking areas. Walk facing traffic. These cautions seem simplistic and obvious, but often a short-cut through the parking lot seems more appealing than walking around it via the street.

USE THE BUDDY SYSTEM

Most attacks on women take place one on one. Why? Because the predator understands that the more people he has to deal with, the less likely he will be able to control the situation. Whenever possible, walk or run with a friend. Alternatively, walk with a dog. No matter what size the dog is, it will reduce your risks. Dogs make noise and can bite—too much trouble for the average predator.

DRESS STREETWISE

Purses, Bags, and Packs

Your purse says "Target." If you must carry a purse or bag, sling it over your neck and shoulder and slightly in front of you with the flap facing your body. By doing so, you are less likely to be the victim of a purse snatching. If you cannot sling your purse or bag in this way, carry it under your arm like a football, keeping it close to your body. The bigger the purse or bag that you are carrying, the more likely it is you will be targeted. In the street predator's mind, bigger means more. Alternatives to a purse include hip sacks (or fanny packs) and back packs. These items have two primary advantages: they are secured to the body, thus making them difficult to grab; and both of your arms and hands are free, allowing for physical self-defence if necessary.

Limit Your Load

Do not burden yourself with packages, totebags, shopping bags, etc. This marks you as a target, and more importantly, restricts the use of your hands and arms if needed for defence. Accept offers of or ask for assistance from store employees if you feel vulnerable or overburdened getting to your car.

Clothing

Constrictive clothing and shoes severely limit your chances of running or escape. Wear appropriate footwear—flat, comfortable shoes or runners—and carry your work shoes in your pack. If you wear heeled shoes and find yourself in a situation where you have to run, kick them off. If you are wearing a skirt, dress, or coat that drops below the knees, hike it up so you can run faster.

Umbrellas, high collars, sunglasses, scarves, and hats can limit your vision. Ensure that you can always scan your surroundings, no matter what you are wearing.

Avoid displaying ostentatious or expensive jewellery when walking on the street or when in an otherwise potentially vulnerable situation.

If out at night, and if possible, wear clothing that is bright in colour and easily seen. Carry a pocket-sized flashlight with you, and make sure it is easily accessible. You can use it not only to find your way, but can also shine it in an attacker's face and use it as a weapon.

The Street "Interview" — Are You Being Sized Up?

Most attacks do not follow the sensational television and movie scenario of a mugger jumping out of the bushes at you. In most cases, your attacker will be known to you, or will make some sort of "legitimate" contact prior to attacking. The street predator is very selective in choosing his victim. A fundamental strategy used for his choice is the "interview," a screening method to determine if you are aware of what he is up to, and if you will make an easy target. Being aware of these methods, some very subtle and others extremely intimidating, and how to deal with them, will help you to avoid becoming a victim.

THE "REASONABLE REQUEST" INTERVIEW

In this approach, the predator will make contact with you by means of a reasonable request, such as:

"Do you have the time?"
"Do you have a match/cigarette?"
"Spare any change?"

While asking this, the predator is carefully observing you. If you comply, by looking at your watch or finding a lighter, the predator takes advantage of your distraction and moves into position for a surprise attack, such as a purse snatching.

Defence: When a stranger asks you these types of questions, very politely but firmly answer him by saying, "Sorry, I cannot help you." If you are not polite or ignore the person, he may become hostile towards you. If you do decide to answer the questions, put distance or a barrier between you and him.

THE "BUZZ" INTERVIEW

The "buzz" interview is related to the "reasonable request" interview, and is a tactic primarily employed by the young and inexperienced street predator. In this encounter, a person will attempt to get as close to you as possible, usually from the rear. He is testing your awareness level of his presence. The closer he can get undetected, the more likely he will be able to get away with a crime such as assault or robbery.

Defence: If you suspect someone is "buzzing" you, immediately face him and make eye contact. When the predator realizes that you know he is there, he will usually back off or veer away in another direction in search of another target. Awareness of your surroundings is the best method of prevention in this type of approach.

THE "DISTANT" INTERVIEW

Criminals frequently use this method to choose their victims. Unlike the "reasonable request" or "buzz" interview, in which the predator makes direct contact, the predator carrying out a "distant" interview, while in plain view, assesses a potential victim from a distance by studying body language (head down, slouched, burdened with parcels, unaware, etc.). Most victims fail to recognize the threat, simply because they are not paying attention.

Defence: Be aware of your surroundings at all times. When walking, use force presence and make brief eye contact with people around you. Don't appear to be a victim.

THE "BULLY" INTERVIEW

This is a common approach and can evolve rapidly into a dangerous situation, especially if the predator is with a group of peers. In the encounter the predator will aggressively demand to know such things as "What are you looking at?" or make crude remarks such as "Nice ass, baby." The sole intent of the question is to try to elicit a negative response from you, such as "Not much" or "Piss off," so he can have a reason to retaliate. A negative response indicates a challenge, thus validating the reason he was looking for to attack you. If the person is with peers, there may be an obligation to "save face" under this perceived challenge, and a physical confrontation will almost certainly follow.

Defence: Do not play into the street predator's hand. Learn to ignore cat-calls, wolf whistles, coarse language, intimidating comments, and challenges. Simply keep walking in a calm manner.

CHAPTER THREE

If an Attack Happens

Canadian Law—Do You Know Your Rights?

Many women are concerned that if they fight back to defend themselves, they may be opening themselves to legal consequences. When it comes to using physical force for self-defence, the Criminal Code of Canada outlines the legal constraints on using force specific to an unprovoked assault.

Section 34(1) of the Criminal Code says:

> Everyone who is unlawfully assaulted without having provoked the assault is justified in repelling force by force if the force he uses is not intended to cause death or grievous bodily injury and is no more than is necessary to enable him to defend himself.

Section 34(2) of the Criminal Code further says:

> Everyone who is unlawfully assaulted and who causes death or grievous bodily harm in repelling the assault is justified if:

- He causes it under reasonable apprehension of death or grievous bodily harm from the violence with which the assault was originally made or with which the assailant pursues his purpose; and

- He believes on reasonable grounds, that he cannot otherwise preserve himself from death or grievous bodily harm.

In other words, Section 34 of the Criminal Code gives you the legal authority to defend yourself if:

● You did not provoke the assault;

● You used no more force than was necessary and reasonable to defend yourself;

● You only used force that was likely to cause death or grievous bodily injury if you believed you were going to be seriously injured or killed; and

● You had no other reasonable options available to you other than to physically defend yourself.

Section 37(1) of the Criminal Code says:

> Everyone is justified in using force to defend himself or anyone under his protection from assault, if he uses no more force than is necessary to prevent the assault or the repetition of it.

Section 37(2) of the Criminal Code further says:

> Nothing in this section shall be deemed to justify the wilful infliction of any hurt or mischief that is excessive, having regard to the nature of the assault that the force used was intended to prevent.

Section 37 of the Criminal Code gives you the legal authority to defend yourself or anyone else under your protection, such as family and friends, if:

● You used only as much force as necessary and reasonable to prevent or prolong an assault; and

● The amount of force you used was not excessive in relation to the nature and level of force you were faced with.

Sections 34 and 37 are known as the "Self-Defence" sections of the Criminal Code of Canada, and they give you the authority to physically defend yourself if necessary.

Although many women believe that they have to wait for an attacker to do something physically to them first before they defend themselves, this is not true. These two Criminal Code sections also allow you to strike an attacker first, when you reasonably believe, based upon your attacker's words and or actions, that he is going to be, or is, a physical threat to you. So if you are faced with a person whom you identify as a threat to your personal safety, you may strike first in self-defence, as you have both the legal and moral right to do so.

Self-Defence Training—Pros and Cons

Because women are increasingly concerned for their safety in today's violent world, many groups and individuals have responded by teaching what they call "self-defence" courses for women.

Unfortunately, many women's self-defence programs are nothing but watered-down martial arts courses and do not prepare a woman for real-world self-defence situations. Most techniques being taught as "Women's Self-Defence," will fail under the stress of an actual attack. Why? Because the techniques taught are far too complex and not easily remembered. They involve complicated moves and strategies and require constant practices and skill upgrades. Techniques taught in some programs tend to be "politically correct," while your attacker's strategies are not.

It is important to evaluate the goals and practical usefulness of a women's self-defence program before making a commitment. When doing so, you would be wise to consider the following guidelines:

● Avoid martial arts studios unless you specifically wish to train in the traditional martial arts techniques and are prepared for a long-term commitment.

● The self-defence program should include simulated assaults to allow women to actually practise what they have learned. A good program will have a fully padded instructor in realistic rape and attack scenarios. If a program does not offer this type of training, then it is not adequately preparing you for the reality of the street.

● The self-defence techniques taught should follow the **SAFE** principle:

S imple to use and easily learned and remembered over time.

A daptable to any physical confrontation, be it walking, running, driving, sitting, or lying down.

F ast—the techniques taught must be designed to immediately incapacitate (stun) an attacker, thus allowing you a chance to escape (run). Your goal is not to win the confrontation, but rather to survive it, both physically and mentally.

E ffective—the techniques taught should be 90% effective on 90% of the population 90% of the time. Nothing is ever 100% effective in self-defence. An instructor who claims otherwise is not dealing with reality and should be avoided.

● The self-defence program should incorporate the psychology of combat into the training. The mind guides the body. If you fail to train your mind to cope and deal with fear, regardless of the physical skills learned, you will not be able to defend yourself.

Women should be encouraged to defend themselves. A woman's safety begins and ends with her. By learning realistic self-defence techniques, women are best preparing themselves, both physically and mentally, to survive an assault.

If You Are Confronted—The Basics

Even if you are protecting yourself by being alert and aware of who and what is around you, it is a sad reality that you still may find yourself faced with an attacker. As mentioned earlier, the attacker could want your property, your body or, rarely, your life. There are a number of tactical response options available to you: escape the situation; create noise and attract attention; obey the attacker; defuse or negotiate the situation; and physically defend yourself (with or without weapons). Which choice or choices you make will depend on what the attacker wants from you and what you sense is appropriate for the situation. Remember, your goal is not to be "right"—it is survival.

Escape

YOUR FIRST AND BEST OPTION

When confronted with a potentially dangerous circumstance, your first and best option is always to *get away*. Self-defence does not necessarily mean to stand there and get into a physical confrontation with a potential attacker. Self-defence means to get away as quickly as possible when you recognize you are in a dangerous situation. Escape routes include cars, buses, windows, doors, stores and businesses, stairs, bushes, over walls and fences and gates. Run and yell for help. Remember to listen to your intuition in assessing the danger of the situation—if you don't feel safe, you're probably right. Act on it before you are in serious trouble. Even if you are incorrect, the only repercussion is perhaps slight embarrassment.

DON'T LEAVE THE PRIMARY CRIME SCENE!

What if the unthinkable happens: you are suddenly confronted by a predator who demands that you go with him, be it in a car, or into an alley, a building. It would seem rational, if not prudent, under the circumstances and threat of impending immediate death to obey the attacker. *You must not go with him.* If you do accompany him, your chances of being seen alive again are slim. Even if the attacker claims he will not hurt you if you do what he says, do not believe him: he intends harm. *Do not go.* Immediately run away. Here's why:

The place where you have been accosted is, in police terminology, the "primary crime scene." The place you are being forced to go is called the "secondary crime scene." The primary crime scene is usually a more dangerous area for the predator, as he has less control over you and the surroundings, and he may be seen or heard and reported to police by witnesses. The secondary crime scene has been chosen by the attacker for its seclusion and his safety, a place where he will have complete dominance over you and the situation. Here, his risks of being caught are minimal, and your likelihood of survival is small.

The reality is that you are far more likely to be killed or seriously injured if you go with the predator than if you run away. A situation of being forced into a car at gunpoint appears to be a Catch-22 (he'll shoot me if I don't; he'll shoot me if I do). However, the odds are heavily in your favour if you resist (see "Defend Yourself," below, for statistical evidence).

Create Noise and Attract Attention

A powerful tool you can use to your advantage in making an escape is to create noise. By making as much noise as possible, you are drawing attention to yourself and the attacker, a situation the attacker does not welcome. Even if the attacker claims he will not hurt you if you remain quiet, do not believe him. You are much more likely to be assaulted or injured if you stay silent.

Remember that the predator needs to be in control of both you and the situation at all times. Creating noise gives you a strong advantage in taking away part of this control. By making a lot of noise, you demonstrate to him that you are in command of what happens to you. You are no longer the easy and compliant victim he thought you were. Also, because the noise will draw the attention of others, his risk of being caught is higher, and he may run away. By making noise, you have destroyed his total control of you and the situation.

SHOUTING

Yelling "help" is one of the simplest and most effective methods of attracting attention. Someone may either come to your aid, or call 9-1-1. Police report that their switchboards light up when a woman yells for help. Calls for help can be heard for a surprising distance, for instance, three or four houses away, or in an apartment three floors away. Do not scream "fire." This will not get the response that "help" does. Yelling also forces you to breathe, drawing in the necessary oxygen to the brain and muscles so they can function to help you think and defend yourself. Yelling is preferable to screaming, as the latter is unspecific and may, at a distance, be mistaken for children playing. However, making *any* noise is still better than no noise at all.

CAR HORNS

If confronted in your car and you cannot drive away, lean on the horn and stay on it.

THUMPING, BANGING, THROWING, BREAKING

An assault situation is not a time to be polite or considerate of possessions or property. Depending on where you are—in an apartment or on the street—use whatever means you can to make noise and attract attention. Bang on adjoining apartment walls, throw books or a lamp or whatever comes to hand through a window or against a wall or at the attacker. Stomp on the floor. On the street, use whatever is there—a rock, brick, bottle, shoe heel—and throw it through a window of a building or car. This will create a lot of noise, especially if the building or car has an alarm system.

WHISTLES

Save your whistle breath to yell instead. Safety whistles for self-defence only work where a designated whistle program is in effect, such as at certain colleges or universities. When you hear a whistle, many possibilities come to mind: someone training a dog, a police officer, sports events, children playing. Safety whistles are, however, useful and indeed recommended as communication devices in the woods, or as a "person overboard" alert on boats. Also, for someone with a physical challenge, a safety whistle may be their lifeline.

PERSONAL ALARMS

With the siren sounding on your personal alarm and the piercing noise penetrating the air, you would expect citizens or police to quickly come to your aid. However, personal alarms, although loud, sound like car alarms. Most police departments do not attend car alarm calls because they occur so frequently and the majority prove to be false. As well, the average citizen would regard a siren that sounds like a car alarm as a nuisance, and not a person needing help. Save your money. If the attacker were to cup his hand over the alarm, or simply throw it to the ground and smash it, or if your batteries were to die, your electronic cry for help is instantly diminished. Use your voice to sound the alarm and not a mechanical device that may only give you a false sense of security.

Obey

In a confrontation in which an attacker demands your purse, wallet, car keys, or other material things, give them to him; money and other items can be replaced. Never hand over your property directly. Try to maintain as great a distance as possible and throw the item(s) one way, while you run the other way, yelling for help. If the attacker really wants your property, he will go and retrieve it, thus giving you a chance to escape. If he doesn't, you now know he wants more from you than just your property, and you have a head start in getting away.

Defuse or Negotiate

The longer you interact with an attacker who is a stranger, the more likely you will be the victim of an assault. In such situations, the sooner you react by running away or physically defending yourself, the better. Conversely, if the attacker is known to you, negotiating or talking your way out may be advantageous, buying you time to escape or plan a physical defence.

Defend Yourself

Many women worry that they will anger their attacker even more, and get hurt worse, if they fight back. However, some statistics regarding sexual assault illustrate the advantages of fighting back. Recently, major studies on sexual violence were conducted by the University of Minnesota, Stanford University, University of Nebraska-Omaha, and Brandeis University. All concluded that in each case in which a woman succeeded in escaping a sexual attack, it was the woman's forceful resistance that prevented the assault. Further, women who defended themselves were less likely to be raped and no more likely to be injured than those who resisted weakly or not at all. It was also found that women who took preventative measures such as fighting back, yelling, or running away were far more likely to emotionally cope with the mental trauma. A 1991 statistical analysis by the United States Department of Justice reported that 71% of the women respondents were able to avoid rape by taking defensive actions.

At this point, you might ask, "What if he has a weapon?" Generally, if a predator is armed, he is using the weapon as a tool to intimidate his victim into submission. Fewer than 1% of attacks on women in Canada actually involve a weapon of any kind. Of those predators who carry a weapon, still fewer will decide to pull it; still fewer will actually use it; and still fewer will actually manage to injure or kill you with it. In fact, even in the U.S., where guns are much more common, fatalities occur in only about 1% of all crimes that involve handguns. Remember the situation of being forced into a car at gunpoint? It is highly unlikely that the predator would try to shoot you if you ran away, but even if he did, bullets travel a straight line, and it is *extremely* difficult even for experienced shooters to hit a moving target. (For this reason, run away in a zigzag pattern when a gun is involved.) For knives, clubs, etc. running away immediately is an even better idea, as the chance is miniscule that such weapons would be thrown at you and hit you. By contrast, you will almost certainly be hurt badly or even murdered if you obey the predator.

The following are statistics regarding weapon use by attackers and survival of victims compiled by Michael Rand in his 1990 report, "Handgun Crime Victims," prepared for the Bureau of Justice Statistics in the United States. These real statistics may further influence your choice to resist.

● In 93% of all rapes, no gun was used.

● Of the 99% of all violent crimes involving handguns where there were no fatalities, 87% of the guns were never fired, 85% of the victims were not injured, 10% received minor injuries, and only 2% were shot. Of those who were shot, only 21% were hospitalized for three or more weeks.

● In 78% of all assaults involving attackers with knives, the knife was never used. Attempted stabbings were reported in 12% of all the assaults where knives were present with only 10% of all attackers stabbing their victims.

● ● ●

If you find yourself in a confrontation, apply the following principles:

● Attempt to physically defend yourself only when you have no other choice, and it is apparent that other options such as running away and negotiation are not going to work.

● Defend yourself physically only when you feel you are in immediate danger.

● Defend yourself physically only for the purposes of escaping a dangerous situation.

Be assured that you have both the moral and legal right to physically defend yourself, even though the attacker may not have struck first.

This book does not describe physical self-defence techniques; they are better taught in a self-defence course. However, if you do find yourself in a situation in which you decide to fight back, a few important physical and mental principles you should know about are described below. A good self-defence course will incorporate and expand on these basic elements.

The most effective way to disable an attacker is to focus on the most vulnerable areas of his body, which are:

Vision
The eyes should be your primary target. If a person can't see, he can't fight. Even better, if blinded, an attacker will be unable to chase you.

Wind/Groin
If you cannot attack his eyes, go for the "wind" areas, such as the throat. If a person can't breathe, he will have a hard time fighting or running after you. Many women believe that the groin is the most important target, but it is *not*. Men will consciously protect their groin because they know women are taught to attack this sensitive area. The groin, however, is a good secondary target once the eyes have been attacked, since the attacker's attention is now elsewhere and his groin is unprotected.

Limbs
The legs, and specifically the knees, are other key focus areas. It takes only about 55 pounds of pressure to dislocate or even break a knee joint, if struck properly. *Any* woman with the use of her arms or legs is capable of doing this if shown how in a creditable self-defence program. Not only will your attacker be in a great deal of pain, but he will be unable to run after you as you make your escape.

In terms of mental tactics, the element of surprise is crucial in most confrontations. Your attacker uses it to his advantage; you should as well. If your force presence (assertive posture, telling him to "back off," etc.) has failed, and it appears inevitable that you will be attacked and injured, it is essential not to panic, but to think about how you can regain some control in the situation. The best approach in such cases is obviously to immediately strike first. However, if you miss this opportunity (for instance, if he already has a knife to your throat, or if you are in an acquaintance rape situation in which you are isolated with him), it may be to your advantage to let him believe you are indeed weak and helpless, until you can get in a powerful strike and catch him totally off guard. Remember, the predator believes you are his "prey." If you give the predator any advance warning that you are going to strike back, he will be better able to prepare his own defense, and will probably take a more aggressive approach than he might have otherwise. Acting like "prey" ("Please, don't hurt me") may buy you time in planning a good surprise attack, and is certainly better than wearing yourself out struggling when he has you immobilized.

Consider Using Self-Defence Tools

GENERAL GUIDELINES

Many women wonder if they should carry some sort of weapon to help defend themselves. If you choose to fight back using a self-defence tool, keep in mind that it is only as good as the training you have received to use it. Do not carry a self-defence weapon unless you have been properly trained by a professional instructor. By doing so, you are ensuring you can use the tool to its full potential and that you understand its limitations. If you have not received adequate training and find yourself in a situation where it is necessary to pull the tool, chances are great that the attacker will grab the weapon and use it against you.

Follow these guidelines when using self-defence tools:

● Make sure the self-defence tool is legal to carry.

● A self-defence tool does not replace thinking. Far too often, reliance and trust are placed on the tool alone, and when it isn't effective, people panic and get hurt.

● Never carry a self-defence tool unless you are confident in how to use it. Avoid items that can hurt you when you use them; for example, car keys held interlaced in the fingers are likely to break your fingers if you strike someone. (See also under Pepper Spray, below.)

● Never carry a self-defence tool unless you intend to use it in a dangerous situation and you understand the legalities and consequences of using it.

● Do not display or pull out a self-defence tool unless you are prepared to use it *immediately*. If you don't, your attacker will take it and use it against you.

● Do not use a self-defence tool unless you are prepared and willing to use it ruthlessly. Generally, you will only get one chance.

PEPPER SPRAY

In the past several years, pepper spray has become very popular and many Canadian women now carry it. When sprayed in an attacker's face, pepper spray makes breathing difficult and causes an intense burning sensation to the eyes, temporarily blinding an affected person.

Pepper spray was first developed in the United States in the early 1970s. Originally intended as a food additive (it is derived from compounds in hot peppers), its potential as an alternative to chemical-based mace soon became apparent. Although pepper spray can be a very effective self-defence tool, most women are not informed of its limitations. Consider the following:

● Did you know that pepper spray doesn't work on everyone? It has a surprisingly high failure rate: 15–20% of people will not be incapacitated even by a full-face spray. If you happen to be up against one of those unaffected, an attacker's anger will surely heighten and you will likely panic as a result.

● What about its legalities? At present, pepper sprays designed to be used against *animals* are legal to possess in Canada, but this ruling is always subject to change, depending upon current legislation. Pepper sprays designed to be used against *humans* are illegal to possess and a prohibited weapon in Canada. Having said this, if a women were to defend herself from an attacker by using pepper spray, it is highly unlikely that charges would be laid against her. However, if she sprayed someone who merely annoyed her, she would be criminally liable for her actions. The only time you would be justified in using pepper spray is when you perceived a real threat, to yourself or others in your charge, of serious injury or death from an attacker.

● Have you ever tested it? You need to know it will work if required. It does have a shelf life; it won't last forever. Just like other sprays, the spout could get clogged. Pepper spray should be tested once a month.

● Do you know how far it reaches? In general, a lipstick-size container will reach 1.5–2 m (5–7 ft), and a larger canister has a range of 4.5–6 m (15–20 ft) or more.

● Do you know how the spray is delivered—in a straight stream, or cone-shaped to saturate a larger area? In the stress of an attack, a stream requires more precision. Cone-shaped sprays are easier to use as you don't have to be so accurate.

● Will you yourself be affected by the spray? You may be adversely affected or even incapacitated by the spray in certain environments. A closed-in room would mean all inside would feel the effects. If outside, make sure you know which way the wind is blowing.

● Are you prepared to carry the pepper spray so it is readily accessible? You should carry it either in your hand or in a holster for quick access. Fumbling in your bag will only waste time and alert the attacker to your intentions.

Remember, pepper spray is an excellent self-defence tool; however, it does have its limitations and liabilities. If it fails, you better have another option available, such as hands-on self-defence techniques, with which to defend yourself. You don't want to panic and freeze.

IMPROVISED WEAPONS

If you are being physically attacked, use whatever self-defence TOYS are around you to give you an advantage. TOYS stands for "Tools Of Your Surroundings." The following are some improvised TOYS to keep in mind.

Improvised Impact Weapons. Improvised impact weapons are those objects which are commonly found and which can be used to hit an attacker to harm him or distract him temporarily.

Examples include:

- crowbar
- sticks, rocks
- flashlight
- telephone
- 2 × 4, baseball bat
- lamp, chair

- bar table, bar stool
- beer mugs, ashtrays
- bicycle
- garbage can
- pool ball or cue
- briefcase, umbrella

Use *any* common item close at hand which has weight behind it and which you can use to effectively strike your attacker.

Improvised Distraction Weapons. Improvised distraction weapons are those objects and items which can be thrown at an attacker, to temporarily distract him so that you can escape. These weapons are usually directed towards an attacker's face or legs.

Some examples:

- spit
- beer, pop, coffee
- keys, coins
- sunglasses, hat
- rocks, sand

- newspaper, magazine, books
- bag, purse, wallet
- cans or glasses
- pager
- comb or brush

Improvised Edged or Pointed Weapons. Edged or pointed weapons are those items which can be used to slash or stab your attacker. These items could include:

- knives, forks
- broken bottles
- scissors
- knitting needles

- screwdrivers
- pens, pencils
- keys
- nails, spikes

Improvised Barriers and Shields. Barriers and shields are objects you can put between yourself and your attacker. These can be used as an obstacle an attacker has to go through to get to you, or for protection against a punch, kick, impact weapon, or edged weapon attack. These items could include:

Barriers

- cars, car doors
- tables, chairs, other furniture
- fence, wall, doors
- mail box
- dumpster

Shields

- briefcase, suitcase, knapsack
- garbage can lid
- bicycle
- skateboard
- roasting pans or lids

Remember, nothing is guaranteed to work. Never depend upon a self-defence tool or "TOYS" to stop an attacker. Your body and wits will always be with you and will provide you with countless creative options under the stress of an actual attack.

Identifying Your Attacker

It is difficult, if not almost impossible, for the average person under stressful circumstances to not only observe but also remember a description of an unknown attacker. Commonly, a number of witnesses to a crime will give an equal number of differing descriptions. A useful tip is to focus on one or two specific identifiers, such as a scar, missing tooth, hair colour/style, etc. More often then not, these specific characteristics will lead police to an arrest.

Recently, a 15-year-old Vancouver Island girl was dragged at knifepoint into undergrowth and sexually assaulted. She was able to provide police with specific identifiers, in this case a distinctive tattoo on the hand, and the suspect was arrested within two days.

Physical information the police will ask you to recall include the following:

- age
- race
- hair colour and length
- accents, pitch of voice
- type of weapon
- direction of travel
- distinctive body odour, breath
- distinguishing characteristics such as jewellery, scars, acne, tattoos

- sex
- height, body size and shape
- presence of facial hair
- specific clothing
- car make, colour, licence number

There are two ways your attacker can be identified:

● If he is known to you; or

● If he is unknown and the police have a suspect, you will be shown a photo line-up usually containing eight individual pictures. If your attacker is one of the eight in the line-up, he would be identified by you as the person responsible.

CHAPTER FOUR

Everyday Safety Strategies

Target-Hardening Your Residence

Outside Your Home

As mentioned, most criminals are lazy animals. Knowing this, make it difficult for an intruder by making your home a **HARD TARGET**. An intruder's selection process is very simple: he is usually looking for an unoccupied home with the easiest access, the greatest amount of cover to hide his actions, and the best escape route. When a burglar is browsing a neighbourhood, deterrents and home owner management are critical factors in protecting a home. Proper target-hardening will usually persuade the opportunistic thief to choose another home that offers them easier access and fewer risks.

Once a home has been targeted, the burglar will actually spend only about 60 seconds gaining access and no more than about five minutes inside. In most home break and enters, the point of entry is on the ground floor and via the side or back door, with the garage being the second most common entry point. Without a doubt, the three most common characteristics of this crime are:

1 The break and enter usually happens during the daytime.

2 Most targeted homes are a two-person working household.

3 Most break and enters happen between the months of May and September.

Here are some suggestions to target-harden your home:

● Install motion lights or leave your front and rear porch lights on at night. Criminals do not like to be noticed, so the more you light up your home at night, the more you decrease the chance your home will be chosen. Ensure these lights are placed at a height that cannot be easily reached by an intruder. There have been a number of documented cases where criminals have unscrewed or covered up a home's motion and flood lights, thus allowing them to work under the cover of darkness.

● Trim large bushes which cover or hide windows and doors. They also provide cover for an intruder to work behind. The exception to this strategy is to have defensive shrubbery such as large prickly or thorny bushes, a natural form of barbed wire.

● Fences and hedges, although not impassable, act as a deterrent to burglars. Fences and hedges can, however, also conceal burglars. Therefore, a fence you can see through is best.

● Do not store ladders or tools outside. Many burglars have used the homeowner's own ladder to gain access into a second-story window that was left open and the homeowner's own tools to break through a door or window. Motion light sensors, double-locked doors, and other precautions may be useless if a determined thief has your own splitting axe right at hand to break the door down.

● Buckets, benches, patio furniture, etc. should be secured down or stored inside. These items can be used by the intruder instead of a ladder to gain window access.

● Place plants, jars, etc. on balconies or window sills. These create a noisy obstacle course when knocked over, alerting you to the intruder or scaring him off.

● Do not hide house keys anywhere outside the home. Leave them with a trusted neighbour. Thieves know all the usual places (under rocks, mats, or ledges) and are extremely clever at finding the unusual places. For example, one thief in Victoria found keys hidden 20 feet from the residence in a knot-hole of an oak tree.

● If you are a woman living alone, don't use your first name on mailboxes or apartment directory boards. Use your last name only. Do not use "Occupied," as this practice has become so common that it almost invariably indicates a single woman living there.

● Make sure that your street address is visible from the road. This will help emergency personnel find you. Also, do not place your name anywhere on the exterior of your home. It is a common strategy that when prowling a neighbourhood, a thief will look for homes that advertise the occupant's last name. The thief can look that name up in the phone book and find the number that corresponds to the address. He will then walk up to the front door, and with his cell phone dial the number. If there is no answer and he can hear the phone ringing, it is a good indicator that no one is home.

● Ensure that all doors are solid core and can withstand being kicked in. All doors should also be fitted with good-quality deadbolt locks with at least a 3-cm (1.5 inch) bolt throw into the door frame. Even better than, or in addition to, the deadbolt, is a new device called "The Door Block™." This revolutionary new system, designed in Canada, is simple, easily installed, and inexpensive, and it greatly increases your door's "kick-in" resistance. It is recommended by police as a way to help prevent break-ins and home invasions.

● Ensure that the door frame has a solid 10–30 cm (5–10 inch) metal strike plate, which should be mounted with a minimum of six 8-cm (3-inch) screws that pass through the door facing and into the wall stud/frame of the house. The strike plate, which holds the lock bolt from the lock in place, and which comes with most deadbolt locks, is often substandard and is what usually gives way first when a door is forced in by an intruder.

● Install a wraparound steel plate on the front of the door which covers the deadbolt and strike plate. This device will not only strengthen a door's "kick in" factor, but it will also make it extremely hard for an intruder to use a pry tool to pop or shimmy the door open.

● Pin hinges on the outside of exterior doors should be secured with long screws into the frame to prevent a burglar from simply unscrewing the hinges and removing the door.

● If your doors are solid wood, install a peephole that gives you a broad view of who or what is on the other side.

● When moving into a new home or apartment, have all door locks rekeyed. This will cost an average of about $5.00 per lock, a small price to pay for peace of mind and extra security. Contact a local bonded locksmith for more information.

● Basement windows and any ground-floor windows that are hidden from view should be barred or secured with the new types of non-breakable window films now available.

● Sliding doors and windows that can be lifted out of their frames should be installed with anti-lift devices in the upper track. For patio doors, a "swingdown bar" or a "Charley Bar" is an excellent security device and acts as a visual deterrent to a potential intruder. Although sticks placed in the lower tracks work along the same premise as a Charley Bar, they can be defeated easily by a seasoned thief. Sliding glass windows and doors can also be secured with lower track locking devices. All these securing ideas are inexpensive and can usually be installed by the homeowner.

• Ensure that garage doors are closed and locked. If going away for an extended period of time, ensure that the garage door is padlocked from the inside. Remember that once an intruder is inside an attached garage, he has all the time and concealment in the world to work on the inside door to your home.

• *Always* keep doors and windows locked, even if you are at home, inside or outside. Often, but especially during the warmer months, thieves will sneak in a front door while you are out in the back gardening or doing other things (hence the nickname "Green Thumb Burglars").

• Use a door wedge instead of a door chain. Chains can be snapped or cut very easily. A door wedge is often stronger than the door it secures.

• Join a neighbourhood or block watch program and get to know your neighbours. Among the best crime prevention tools available to a homeowner are nosy neighbours who will call the police if they see anything suspicious or unusual.

• Get a home security check from your local police department or community police station. Such checks are usually done as a free community service.

Inside Your Home

• Get a dog. Criminals avoid dogs because they make noise and can be aggressive, two things they don't like. If you are unable to keep a dog, there are alarms that attach to door handles that when activated sound like a real dog.

• Take an inventory of the house, room by room, both written and with still photographs or videotape. Keep this inventory somewhere safe and fireproof, preferably a safety deposit box. Update your inventory as required.

• Valuable jewellery and documents that are not in a safety deposit box should be hidden. The bedroom is not a safe place; it is the first room thieves check because they know most valuables are kept there. The kitchen, with many cupboards and shelves, is a good hiding area, as is the basement. There are a number of diversionary home safes on the market that look like cans of pop and other common household products.

● Engrave your driver's licence number on valuables such as stereos, televisions, computers, and tools. An engraving pen can generally be borrowed from the local police department or purchased from a hardware store. "Items marked for identification" stickers for windows and doors are usually provided by the police department.

● Because home computers are prime targets for thieves, back up your hard drive files regularly to ensure you are not out of business if your computer equipment is stolen. Keep the back-up disks in a separate location from the computer. There are also a number of computer securing devices available at most computer stores.

● A cordless phone is useful if you are at home at the time of an attempted break-in. While evading the intruder and reaching a place of safety, you can be dialing 9-1-1. Preferable to the cordless phone is a cell phone ready to use. It is becoming increasingly common for thieves to cut a home's telephone line prior to entering, thus preventing regular telephone access.

● If you are a single woman, refer to yourself as "we" on an answering machine message. You may also wish to subscribe to "call display." Check with your local phone company for information on services that record the phone number and subscriber, as well as the time and date of all calls.

● Before leaving your home, develop the habit of doing a walk-through check of your residence to ensure that all doors and windows are locked.

● Do not discard packing boxes for electronic items such as computers, VCRs, television sets, audio equipment, etc. Left at a curbside, such packaging openly advertises to a potential thief the brand-new goodies inside your home. Cut these boxes up or burn them.

While You Are Away

A quiet house with long grass, permanently closed curtains, and a pile-up of mail, flyers, and newspapers immediately signals that nobody is at home, a perfect opportunity for a thief. A few simple precautions can make your house appear occupied and a bad risk for a break-in.

● Alert trusted neighbours that you are going away and for how long. Ask them to watch for suspicious strangers and to report these people to the police.

● Arrange for someone to pick up the mail, newspapers, and flyers. In some areas you may be able to cancel delivery of these items altogether during your absence.

● Ensure that you have a trusted person check your house every day or at the very least, every 48 hours. Some insurance companies will void their coverage if this is not done. Also check that your insurance coverage is up-to-date, including "replacement insurance." Contact your insurance agent for more information.

● Leave a car in the driveway—if not yours, a friend's or neighbour's.

● If you plan to be away for an extended period, have a reliable house-sitter live in.

● Ensure that your lawn will be cut and garden tended. If either is growing out of control, it is a good indicator to a potential thief that no one is home.

● In the winter months, be aware of tire and foot tracks in the snow that only show people leaving.

● If leaving the home, even for an evening, turn on some lamps and leave a radio and/or television on. These can be put on inexpensive 24-hour timers so that from the outside, as lights go on in one room and off in another, it appears the house is occupied. Also ensure that curtains are closed.

● Do not leave notes or messages on the front door advising when you will be back home. This only tells the criminal how long he has to burglarize your home.

● Invest in a monitored alarm system and have notices displayed on doors and windows.

Note: If you come home to an open house, or when you open the door it is apparent you have been burglarized, *do not enter for any reason*. The intruder may still be inside. Go to a neighbour's and call the police.

Alarm Systems

Although good deadbolt locks and other security devices are very important for home security, any lock or security device can be defeated or bypassed. To ensure that you target-harden your home effectively, a good alarm system is recommended. A potential thief assessing two separate homes, one with an alarm system and one without, will usually pick the home not protected by the alarm.

There are three types of alarm systems on the market:

- motion
- sensor
- a combination of both.

Some systems have the capacity to flash lights on the outside when an intruder enters, in addition to an audible alarm.

In the past, alarm systems were very expensive for the average homeowner to have installed and monitored. Today, a good alarm system for an average-size home can cost under $1,000. As well, monitoring of these alarms by reputable companies can be as low as $25 a month. With the development in wireless technology, home alarm systems can now be installed without the labour-intensive work needed in a hard-wired system, again saving on cost. As an added incentive, home insurance coverage is often available at a lower rate if an alarm system is installed.

Recently, alarm companies have been advertising nationally that they will protect your home and property for only $24.95 monthly, with a five-year contract, and as a part of this deal supply a free alarm system complete with one door contact and one motion alarm. This type of sales pitch is an alarm company's way of getting their salespeople into your front door. Usually after this salesperson has conducted a "security audit" of your home, you learn that you will have to purchase other additional equipment to provide sufficient security protection. The average Canadian home needs two or three door contacts, two or three window contacts, and possibly two or three motion detectors.

To determine the best system for you, compare pricing from local bonded and reputable home alarm companies that will conduct a home visit to discuss your security concerns and tailor a system designed to meet your needs. Shop around, but deal with only companies who have security licences (a requirement in most provinces).

Remember that a solid "target hardening" approach to home security is three pronged:

- Light up inside and outside.
- Have good locks on all doors and windows.
- Have a good alarm system.

Many cities in Canada now have alarm bylaws that require a homeowner to purchase a permit prior to installation of a home alarm system. A condition of this permit may be a "fee for service" that will be levied against the homeowner should a false alarm take place and police attend. Contact your local police department to find out if a permit is required in your area.

Strangers at the Door

● Never open your door to a person you don't know. This is how most home invasions begin.

● Speak to salespeople through the door; they are used to this and chances are you do not want their products or service anyway. Relatively inexpensive intercoms for doors are now available.

● Do not allow repair persons inside your house or apartment until you have confirmed the validity of the visit with their company or unless you have pre-arranged the appointment yourself. In one real incident, thieves took pains to imitate an established repair service, even painting their truck appropriately, and successfully gained entry into and robbed a number of households this way. Check credentials through a window or the door peephole, or have them slide their business card under the door. Be aware, however, that business cards are easily duplicated or falsified.

● If you live in an apartment and a repair person tells you his/her visit was arranged by the manager, confirm with the manager before allowing entry.

● If leaving a secured apartment block, do not allow anyone access as you are leaving. Secure the door and let the people outside be buzzed in by the tenants they are visiting.

● Some predators impersonate police officers. In Surrey, a home invasion was perpetrated by individuals who had obtained second-hand RCMP uniforms from an army surplus store. If an officer requests entrance to your home, look carefully at the uniform, ensure he or she is driving a marked police vehicle, and ask him/her to provide a badge and police identification number. If you feel at all unsure about the true identity of a person claiming to be a police officer, contact your local police department to ensure the visit is legitimate.

● Report any suspicious persons or irregular activity in your neighbourhood to police; for instance, strangers knocking on doors. This is how many crimes are prevented and solved.

● Be aware that some predators impersonate delivery personnel (florists, couriers, etc.) or door-to-door canvassers (charities and other non-profit activities). Do not open the door until you have established the validity of the visit. With deliveries, for example, ask through the door for the name of the addressee (i.e., you) and the name of the sender. If the person cannot provide you with your own name, be extremely suspicious. Unless you must sign for the delivery (in which case be extra careful), ask them to leave the item outside for you. Similarly, for charities, ask them to leave an envelope with the relevant information outside (a legitimate charity will be willing and able to do this).

Home Invasions

THE CRIME OF THE 90s

Home invasions have become "the" crime of the late 1990s. Common in other parts of the world, such as Brazil, they are a relatively new occurrence in Canada. The reason for a home invasion is similar to that for a break and enter: stealing money or jewellery or other valuables that can be sold quickly for immediate cash with few traces. In both break and enters and home invasions, often the residence is trashed, either in the ransacking or for the dubious pleasure of causing destruction. There is no disputing the damaging psychological effects a break and enter has on people returning home to discover their residence has been broken into by strangers. However, home invasions are marked by the additional trauma of direct, abusive contact with the intruders.

After a home invasion, the psychological impact on victims and their families, particularly when older people are the chosen targets, is immeasurable and devastating. Victims rarely feel safe or even comfortable in their own homes again. Their sense of security is violently shattered, leading in some cases to severe health problems such as heart attacks and mental breakdowns. This extremely cruel and brutal crime has the public angry and frightened. Law enforcers are frustrated by the lack of leads to suspects and arrests.

In most home invasions, the criminals (usually two people, normally dressed) get into the house simply by knocking at the door. Often a woman knocks at the door, while a man hides nearby. The unsuspecting occupant opens the door and is immediately forcefully overpowered. People in the house are bound with duct tape or rope and moved into one room, where they are terrorized, sometimes at gun or knifepoint and threats of injury, into revealing the locations of their valuables. The criminals are sometimes in the home for hours.

Why are home invasions on the increase? Quite simply, because it is a very easy crime to commit. The invaders use the tactics of total surprise and force to gain entry. They can then maintain complete control over the victims and the situation for as long as they wish without interference by neighbours or police. This crime has reached a particularly ugly and sinister level in the Vancouver area, where most home invasion victims are the elderly. This crime is truly cowardly. The elderly tend to be more trusting and open doors more readily; they are often frail and more easily physically overpowered; they have more ready cash on hand; and they are less likely to resist.

To prevent a home invasion, follow the home-securing strategies listed above, and most importantly, *do not open your door* unless you know who is on the other side. However, in the event that you do become a victim of this crime, the following suggestions will help you stay as safe as possible under the circumstances.

● Familiarize yourself with your home in the dark so you can get through it quickly to escape from a night intruder either to the outside or to your "safe room" (see below).

● If you hear someone attempting to get into your home, or if the intruder is already inside, get out as soon as possible. Do not waste valuable time attempting to find your phone to call police, as by the time you do, the intruder will in all likelihood be inside and on you. Once outside, go to a neighbour's and call police.

● If you cannot get out, you need to call 9-1-1 immediately. Even if the intruder is able to take the phone from you and either hang it up or rip it out of the wall, most police 9-1-1 systems will print out the address from where the call was made and send a patrol car to investigate.

● If you are unable to escape or make it to your safe room and now find yourself bound, you must comply with the intruders' demands. If you do not comply, you are placing yourself at high risk to be seriously injured. Remember, property can be replaced; your life cannot.

YOUR SAFE ROOM

If someone does break in and you are taken by surprise and cannot get out, go to your SAFE ROOM. Every residence should have a safe room, a secure area to which you can retreat to buy time if an intruder is in the house. Typically this would be the master bedroom. The door, preferably solid, should have a deadbolt lock and door wedge or Door Block™ on the inside. There should be another phone (a cell phone is better) and a can of pepper spray and/or fire extinguisher ready for use. Once inside the safe room, close, bolt, and wedge the door shut and call 9-1-1. If the intruder attempts to break through the bedroom door, yell that you are on a cell phone to the police. If the intruder persists and is able to break down the door before police come, immediately use the pepper spray or fire extinguisher and then escape to a neighbour's while yelling for help. If your safe room is to be your child's room, ensure the items for use and the inside bolt are out of the child's reach. Go over your safe room plan with all members of the house as you would your fire escape route.

Many community police and RCMP stations are offering free information sessions to the public regarding this vicious crime. If you don't see one advertised, inquire at your local police station.

Vehicle Smarts

Auto Theft: Some Facts

● Motor vehicle theft and theft from motor vehicles has increased an average of 14% per year in Canada. Stats Canada reports from 1998 indicate that auto theft rates are now higher in Canada than in the United States.

● Most cars are stolen or broken into by young offenders, and most incidents occur in front of the car owner's home.

● In British Columbia, 50 stolen vehicle claims are made on average every day of the year. These losses amount to approximately five million dollars annually.

● Vehicles are stolen whenever opportunities arise. More than 70% of all auto thefts occur between 1:00 a.m. and 5:00 a.m.

The top stolen vehicle makes in North America are:
- Dodge / Plymouth / Chrysler Mini Vans
- Honda Accord
- Toyota Camry
- Oldsmobile Cutlass / Supreme / Ciera
- Honda Civic / CRX
- Ford Mustang
- Toyota Corolla
- Chev full-size pickup / Ford F150 series trucks
- Jeep Grand Cherokee
- Acura Integra

The four main reasons for auto thefts are (in no order):
- joyriding; "for the fun of it"
- transportation
- to commit a crime, e.g., a bank robbery, so that the getaway vehicle cannot be connected with the perpetrator
- commercial theft; "the chop shop" (air bags are particularly big on the black market)

Target-Hardening Your Vehicle

AUTO THEFT

To make your vehicle difficult to steal:

● Close all windows, lock all doors, and never leave keys in the ignition. Do not be complacent when you park your vehicle in the garage or driveway; remember that most vehicle thefts occur in front of the home.

● Never leave a spare car key under the carpeting, in the sunvisor, or magnetically attached under the car frame. These are common places car thieves will look first. Private security company videos from Vancouver show thieves running their hands along wheel wells and underneath frames of vehicles, looking for the magnetic holders. Keep your extra keys in your pocket or wallet instead.

● Always keep the garage door locked.

● Invest in an audible alarm or vehicle disabling system and have it installed professionally. Select a system that comes with a guarantee and an installer who offers a warranty.

● Use a steering column or wheel-locking device.

● Register your vehicle with a CAT (Combat Auto Theft) program at your local insurance company or police department. The car owner places a CAT sticker in the rear window of the car. This sticker gives police the registered owner's permission to stop and check the occupants of the car between the hours of 1:00 a.m. and 5:00 a.m. This program is free, and statistics have shown that owners displaying the CAT decal experience 46% fewer auto thefts than those who do not participate in this program.

● Use a "secure-a-car" VIN (Vehicle Identification Number) etching on all windows. The VIN is already stamped on many places on your vehicle (windshield, inside of door, on engine parts) and it is useful to police in tracing stolen cars or car parts. However, etching it on all windows will act as an additional deterrent to thieves who are stealing your car for resale, since they would now have to replace all the windows.

The best way to protect your vehicle from being stolen is to layer its protection with visual, physical, and auditory (alarm) deterrents. These categories are not mutually exclusive. Visual protection includes not only alarm decals, CAT decals, etc. but also physical safeguards such as steering wheel locks. The mere suggestion of an anti-theft device is often enough to make a potential thief pass your vehicle by in favour of an unprotected target. Physical barriers, ranging from simply locking the car to sophisticated vehicle disabling devices, take time to overcome, and ideally (for the thief!) the theft will take place in a matter of seconds (most thefts, in fact, do). Anti-theft devices often have the added advantage of giving you lower insurance rates.

If your vehicle is stolen you should notify your local police department and insurance agency immediately and be able to provide them with the following information:

- vehicle licence number
- vehicle identification number
- year, make, model, and colour of vehicle
- any distinguishing features of your car such as dents, scratches, decals, etc.
- an inventory of valuable items, tools, etc. and their serial numbers

Copies of all this information should be kept in a safe place outside the vehicle.

THEFT FROM AUTO

Theft of articles from vehicles results in millions of dollars in insurance costs annually and is steadily increasing every year. Although most such thefts occur during the night, they can and do occur any time of the day when a potential thief sees an opportunity.

Some strategies for preventing theft from your vehicle:

● Close windows and lock all doors while the vehicle is left unattended.

● Avoid leaving valuables in a vehicle. If you must do so, lock them in the trunk or conceal them.

● Try to park your vehicle in a busy area or in monitored parking lots.

● Install an alarm system and advertise that you have one by placing stickers on your car.

● Car equipment such as stereos, CB radios, cell phones, and radar detectors are prime targets for thieves. These items should be marked with your driver's licence, and have serial numbers recorded. Many of these items can now be purchased with brackets that allow easy removal when leaving your car unattended.

● Install a locking gas cap to prevent gasoline siphoning.

● Smooth, rounded, door-locking buttons prevent thieves from using coat hangers to get in. Most newer vehicles have this type, but they are inexpensive to install if your vehicle has the older design.

● Many drivers keep parking change in the ashtray and thieves will break in anticipating a haul of money. Leave the ashtray open and empty. Believe it—thieves will break in for parking change or even pop cans.

If your vehicle has been broken into, you should notify your local police department and insurance company immediately and be able to provide them with the following information:

- items stolen and any serial numbers or identifying marks
- the method by which your vehicle was entered

In some cases, the police may attend to see if there is any forensic evidence, such as fingerprints. To avoid destroying evidence, do not touch anything until police say it is all right to do so.

On the Road

● This may seem an obvious point, but it is vitally important that your car is in good working order. Have it serviced regularly. Keep the gas topped up. Have clean windows and lights and properly positioned mirrors for maximum visibility. Don't wait until your vehicle breaks down on a rainy night to find the motivation. Take care of yourself by taking care of your car.

● Join an automobile association.

● Cellular phones are an excellent crime prevention tool. Have one with you for use in emergency situations (but don't leave it in the car!). A cellular phone proved to be a lifesaver for a relative of ours, who was driving home along the 401 near Toronto. When she noticed she was being followed, she tried evasive tactics, but to no avail. The man pulled up beside her, and leered threateningly. She promptly pulled out her cell phone and held it facing him while clearly punching in 9-1-1. He immediately disappeared.

● Keep a pen and paper in your car to record information (licence plate numbers, vehicle descriptions, etc.) that may be relevant to a situation in which you are involved. If you can't reach a pen and paper, be creative—use lipstick or your finger to write on the dash or windshield.

● Be careful what you leave inside your vehicle. Maps indicate you are a tourist (even if you're not) and unlikely to return to the city, therefore a good target for theft. Keep maps in the glove compartment. Valuables (cameras, CDs, purses, luggage, parcels) are easy smash-and-grab items for quick money. These items should be stored in the trunk. Letters or magazines with your address on them should be turned upside down or stored in the trunk. A thief can see where you live and assume you are not home.

● Black out your address on vehicle insurance papers (the address is there only for mailing purposes; police do not need it if they ever ask to see your registration). Car thieves and dishonest parking attendants can use your address to find and then burglarize your unoccupied home.

● Hide garage door openers inside your vehicle. With the knowledge of your address and the garage door opener in hand, a thief has full access into your home.

● Predators are quick to take advantage of your momentary distractions, even actions so simple as getting in and out of your vehicle. Recently, two youths victimized an elderly woman in a mall parking lot in Victoria, snatching her purse as she was getting out of her car. If you see people loitering near your vehicle, do not approach or get out of your car. Have your keys in hand and ready prior to reaching your car.

● Always scan around your vehicle when approaching it, especially underneath it and nearby parked vehicles. Be particularly alert if there is a van or other large vehicle parked near your own. Also, before getting in your car, have a good look inside to ensure nobody is in the car waiting for you.

● Lock all doors and keep windows up when driving, particularly in the downtown areas. This will prevent crimes of opportunity such as car-jackings, purse thefts, assaults on the driver or passengers, etc. Most car-jackings take place when vehicles are stopped at intersections. The criminals approach at a 45-degree angle (in the blind spot), and either pull you out of the driver's seat or jump in the passenger seat.

● Keep your purse under the seat or your knees, out of sight, and not beside you in full view.

● Don't roll the window down more than one inch if you have to talk to someone. Surprisingly little space is needed for someone to reach into your car and grab you or disable your vehicle.

● In traffic, always leave enough space (half a car length) between you and the car in front to allow an escape route if you are confronted.

● If your car breaks down, stay in the vehicle. Turn the hazard lights on. Call for help from a cellular phone. If you don't have a phone, ask whoever stops to call for help. Do not open the window or get out of the car when someone stops; speak through a one-inch window gap.

● Get a HELP POLICE sign. Keep it inside the car. Do not leave it in the trunk. It is of no use to you in an inaccessible place if you are in danger or need help.

● If you have a flat tire, take advantage of your automobile association. If you are not a member, learn how to change a tire so you won't have to sit stranded. If you have a flat in an unsafe place, you can usually continue to drive at a reduced speed until you get to a safe place to stop.

● BUMPING is another crime on the increase. The attacker will intentionally cause a minor accident (usually a rear-ender) with the intent to get you out of your vehicle so that he can either steal your car or attack you. In one incident in a quiet area of Greater Vancouver, a lone woman driver was bumped; when she got out of the car, she was overpowered, dragged into some undergrowth, and sexually assaulted. *Never* get out of your vehicle when involved in a minor accident in an isolated area. Turn your hazard lights on and drive slowly to a busy place. If the bump was legitimate, the other driver will follow. In any case, attempt to get the licence number for police and insurance purposes.

● If you are in your car and confronted by a predator who wants your vehicle, immediately drive away. Even if the predator is armed, it is highly unlikely he will attempt to stop you. If you cannot drive away, lean on the horn until the attacker runs away. If you are confident in its use, have a can of pepper spray or a fire extinguisher ready to go if the attacker tries to get into your car.

● If you are being followed, drive to a busy place such as a gas station, shopping mall, police station, or fire hall, and draw attention by honking your horn and flashing your lights. Never go directly home.

● Do not place your name and address on your keychain. This will give anyone finding your keys easy access into your home. Use a War Amps numbered keychain tag instead. If your keys are found and dropped in a mailbox, the War Amps tag will ensure they are returned to you.

● Never offer a ride to or accept a ride from a stranger. Never hitch-hike or pick up any hitchhikers. Remember that cars are extremely difficult to get out of, and once in a car, you are a prisoner.

Road Rage

It seems that every day we hear on the radio or read in the newspaper about another "road rage" incident that left some-one hurt. So, what is road rage? The National Highways Traffic Safety Administration in the United States says that road rage results "when any high-risk driver combines the anonymity of operating an automobile and the willingness to take out their frustration on anybody at any time."

High-risk drivers, or those most apt to suffer road rage, are those who have a high level of frustration and a low level of concern for fellow motorists. Although studies have shown that some factors make certain people more at risk for road rage, it is important to understand that an out-of-control driver can be anyone on the road, and that you could be victimized by a person in road rage at any time.

No one wants to be a victim of road rage. While you never deserve to be a victim of someone's uncontrolled aggression, there are certain trigger factors you can avoid as a driver to make a road rage incident less likely. For example:

- Do not tailgate.
- Do not cut people off.
- If you are travelling slowly, try to use the right lane.
- Always signal when making a turn or changing lanes.
- Only use your horn when necessary. It is a warning device, not an expression of your state of mind.
- Avoid swearing or rude gestures that may offend other drivers.
- Don't let agitated drivers bother you (but be wary—agitated drivers are potentially dangerous drivers).
- Use low light beams near other vehicles.
- Be courteous; drive the way you would like others to drive.

IF YOU ARE IN A ROAD RAGE SITUATION:

● Make every attempt to get out of the way. If you can't, drive to your local police department or a busy place where you can call police. Don't drive home.

● Do not retaliate. Ask yourself if it is worth personal injury or damage to your vehicle. Put your pride and ego away and do not challenge the other driver. Under no circumstances should you get out of your vehicle or open your window to confront the other driver.

● Be polite and courteous, even if others are not. Ignore gestures and refuse to return them.

● Report the aggressive driver to police via a cell phone if safe to do so, noting the vehicle description, licence number, and direction of travel.

● Remember, a person in road rage has control of a very large weapon, his car, which can be targeted towards you. No matter what, even if you are right, you have to ignore a person in road rage or risk being victimized.

As a police officer, I often encounter road rage reports in my work, but was surprised to experience first-hand a particularly nasty incident. I noticed a driver ahead of me on a wet, busy highway near Victoria pull up beside a loaded school bus and yell profanities. The driver then cut ahead of the bus and braked suddenly several times, causing the bus to fishtail and nearly hit the concrete divider. I pulled up next to the car, flashed my badge, and indicated that he should pull over (even though I was off duty at the time). The driver then focused his rage upon me. He yelled more profanities, hit my car twice with his, and when we drew together, he actually tried to grab me through the windows. In spite of my size, strength, and experience, I did not even consider getting out to confront this man. I drove away to the nearest police station. The man was soon arrested, and his licence was revoked.

Parkades and Lots

● Whenever possible, back into a parking space, so you are pointed in the direction of travel. Although this may take a minute of extra time, you have a quick exit if confronted.

● If you are in a parkade, do not use the stairwells. They are a favourite hangout for potentially dangerous people who often use them to sleep, drink, use illegal narcotics, and have sex. When exiting a parkade after parking, walk out the way you drove in, and walk back in the same way.

● Leave as quickly as possible after reaching your car. The longer you sit, the higher the risk of being approached and confronted.

● Use the vehicle windows as mirrors to see around you as you are getting into the car.

● Your car is not worth dying for. If confronted with a car thief, give him the car. Throw your keys one way while you run the other.

Harassing Telephone Calls

Harassing telephone calls are illegal in Canada—a violation of the Criminal Code.

Most obscene telephone calls are random and the caller wants to shock you. If you receive an obscene phone call, hang up immediately. Do not blow a whistle in the receiver.

● If a caller has the wrong number, ask him what number he was calling. Do not give the caller your own number.

● If you are receiving continual obscene phone calls, call your local police department. The police will start a file and provide you with a case file number. Then contact your local phone company's security division and provide them with the police case number and details of your complaint. The phone company may put a trace on your phone line, and will liaise with police in criminal charges. Throughout the process, keep a careful log of dates and times of all obscene phone calls.

Many phone companies now offer caller identification options. Be aware that these identification options can also be blocked out by a caller. Contact your local phone company for more information.

Purchase an answering machine, which will not only allow you to record all conversations, but also allow you to screen your calls.

Telephone Booths

Phone booths are prime target areas for purse snatchers and thieves. They know your focus is elsewhere and that your arms and hands are not free. Keep your awareness up.

● Never use a phone booth which is in an isolated area.

● If people are loitering near a phone booth, go on to another. Use your intuition.

● Once you have dialled, turn so you have visibility around and behind you. Clear shelter panels in booths can also have a mirror effect; use this to your advantage.

● If using a calling card, protect the number by shielding the phone when you dial.

● You do not need money to dial 9-1-1 from a pay phone.

● Eliminate the problem; invest in a cell phone and use it instead.

Jogging or Walking

To reduce your risks of being attacked, run with another person. SAFETY IN NUMBERS is not a cliché when your own security is at stake.

- Always stay in busy areas where people are around.

- Don't run at night. Exercise in daylight hours, preferably such times as before or after regular work hours, when others are out jogging or walking as well.

- If you do run at night, wear highly visible clothing, stay on busy streets, and carry a flashlight.

- Don't be predictable. Don't run the same route at the same time every day. Vary your schedule.

- If you have a dog, run with it or exercise your neighbour's dog. Predators do not like dogs and will usually target someone else.

- Do not wear headphones. Your sense of hearing is an extremely important tool for ensuring personal safety.

- Ignore all rude comments or verbal harassment. Responding will only elicit trouble, if not a physical confrontation.

- If you are confronted while jogging, yell and scream for help but don't stop running. In Victoria, a number of women were accosted on a popular jogging route by a man with a knife who demanded they go with him. Even though these women had no prior self-defence training, they reacted instinctively by running away and yelling. Doing this probably saved their lives.

- If approached by a predator in a car, turn and run the other way. Report the incident to police. Report any and all details you can recall, such as location, time, licence number, car make and colour, number and description of occupants, etc.

- Always have some personal identification with you. If something does happen to you and you are found unconscious or unable to communicate, this identification could prove to be a lifesaver (medical records, notifying relatives, etc.).

- If you feel comfortable and competent in its use, carry a can of pepper spray in your hand or strapped to your person (it will be next to useless if it is zippered up in a bag). See Chapter 3 for further details on the possession and use of pepper spray.

Automated Teller Machines

Lions and tigers wait in ambush for antelopes to approach the watering hole. Predators and purse-snatchers hang around ATMs waiting for you.

● If possible, don't use an ATM alone; have someone with you. Two people are more difficult for a predator to control than one, and this decreases your risk factor.

● Always be aware of your surroundings prior to using an ATM. Trust your sixth sense. If the situation or people around don't "feel" right, do not use the machine.

● At night, avoid an ATM at a bank or in an isolated area. Use the machines in convenience stores, gas stations, supermarkets, and other busy places.

● Conduct your business as quickly as you can. Constantly check behind and around you.

● As soon as the transaction has been completed, take your money, card, and receipt and immediately leave the area. Do not stand there and count your money. While you are counting, so is the predator.

● If you are confronted while leaving, try to keep a 1.5–2 m (5 ft) distance between you and the attacker. Throw the money one way while you run the other way.

Elevators

● Do not enter an elevator if for any reason you feel unsafe. If you feel uneasy or apprehensive about a passenger, get off the elevator and take the next one.

● Do not press the STOP button if you are confronted. The last thing you want is to be on a stopped elevator with a predator.

● If confronted, yell and scream at the top of your voice. Do not depend upon the elevator alarm to bring you assistance. Most alarms are triggered by kids playing, and most people will ignore the alarm.

● Stand in an advantageous position as illustrated.

  • You have an excellent view of anyone standing outside of the elevator.

  • If you feel uncomfortable about a person entering the elevator, as they move towards the control panel, you have a clear, quick exit from the elevator.

  • If a person does get on the elevator and the doors close, you now have space, however limited, to react defensively if threatened.

Some women's safety programs suggest that you stand beside the elevator button panel. Drawbacks to this can be clearly seen by comparing this position to the recommended illustrated position.

  • You have a poor view of any potential threat outside the elevator.

  • If a person who makes you feel uneasy gets on, that person is blocking your exit.

  • The first thing you expect a person to do when entering the elevator is to push a button. An attacker could feign reaching for the button, but grab you instead, leaving you no time to react.

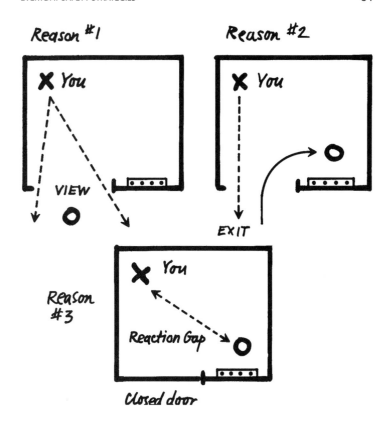

Reason #1

X You

VIEW

Reason #2

X You

EXIT

Reason #3

X You

Reaction Gap

Closed door

Taxi Safety

● Choose a cab company well known in your community. When visiting another city, ask a friend or hotel staff about reputable firms.

● Phone a taxi and wait for it, rather than flagging down the first one that comes along. Wait in a well-lit area.

● Trust your instincts. If you feel uneasy about getting in a particular taxi, do not get in. Phone another cab. If you are in a taxi and get uneasy, get out in a safe place.

● Before getting in, make note of the colour of the cab and cab number. Once inside, also note the name of the driver (most taxi companies now post it).

● Sit in the rear passenger seat. Do not sit beside the driver as this will put you within a vulnerable grabbing distance with no time to react.

● Keep the doors locked, particularly at night. All luggage and packages should go in the trunk.

● At your destination, where appropriate, ask the driver to wait until you are safely inside.

Public Transit

● Weather permitting, it is safer to wait outside of the bus or train shelter. If sitting inside, the walls of the shelter limit your escape in the event of a confrontation.

● Don't daydream, read, or listen to a portable stereo while waiting. Stay alert to the surroundings.

● On the bus or train, sit or stand as close to the driver as possible. On buses, avoid sitting at the back. Move to another place if you are uneasy about another passenger near you.

● Sit on an aisle seat whenever possible. In a number of incidents on Vancouver Island, a molester sat next to (and effectively trapped) women who were sitting in window seats, and began fondling them. As happens in so many cases, once one woman came forward and lodged a complaint, many other women followed suit.

● Most buses have direct communications with the police. Immediately notify the driver to summon police assistance whenever necessary. Also, many cities have mandated their public transit systems to stop for people in danger. If you feel threatened, signal for a bus to stop to pick you up.

● If you feel threatened by another passenger or fear you may be followed after leaving the bus, stay on board and advise the driver of your concerns.

Safety at Work

The Boss's Role

Most provincial Workers' Compensation Boards require that employers have a RISK ASSESSMENT PLAN in effect for their businesses. This plan should outline the action to be taken in the case of an armed robbery, shoplifting, verbal or physical threats to employees or customers, and what to do in case of fire. The following are some safety ideas that an employer can institute to make the workplace safer for all employees.

● Check that all interior and exterior lighting is always in operating order.

● If your business has secondary exit doors, ensure that they are always locked and/or alarmed.

● Pre-program a phone line to immediately call police in an emergency.

● Have phones installed in isolated areas such as back storage rooms.

● Create a safe area with a lockable door, similar to the SAFE ROOM in your residence.

● Install a panic alarm system that is monitored by a reputable alarm company, who will immediately dispatch the police upon activation. These buttons should be placed throughout the building where staff have easy access, and not just at the front counter/till.

● Install a video monitoring system that is always recording during business hours.

● Keep your business well illuminated both inside and outside.

● Ensure that the front counter/till is visible from the front windows.

● Make sure that passers-by can see into your store. Do not place posters or props on your front window(s); visibility by others is a very important safety measure.

● If doing cash drops, do not be predictable. Change the drop times frequently and have someone with you at all times if possible. If you're confronted, the money goes one way while you run the other.

- Instruct employees not to divulge any personal information regarding yourself or other employees.

- Consider joining or initiating a business watch, similar to block watch.

- Talk to staff about their safety concerns. Share with them that their safety is more important to you than making a few dollars. Act upon any immediate safety concerns and praise employees who take appropriate action in any dangerous situation. If your business is large enough, consider forming a safety committee to look at and deal with any safety issues.

The Employee's Role

As an employee, you can increase your safety as follows:

- Be familiar with the RISK ASSESSMENT PLAN at your workplace.

- Know where the emergency exits are located and where you should go if you need to leave the building in an emergency.

- Know where the nearest pay phone is located.

- When closing the business for the night, ensure that all doors are locked and check washrooms and storage areas. Quietly back away if you suspect someone is hiding. Go to the safe area and phone for help.

- Be professional, assertive, and confident when dealing with customers or co-workers.

- If you feel uncomfortable about a customer or co-worker, trust your instincts. Look confident and send a message that you are not intimidated. If things escalate, call a supervisor, security, or the police.

- If you identify someone who is acting suspicious, call security and/or police, and notify other staff.

- Avoid sharing sensitive personal information about yourself with customers or fellow employees.

- If you see someone who makes you feel uncomfortable hanging around at closing, don't leave. Call someone to come and pick you up or contact the police.

- If you are working alone and must verbally confront or challenge a stranger in your workplace, be respectful and never place yourself in a dangerous situation where you may get hurt. Think about calling security or the police.

● If faced with an armed robbery, give the person what he wants. Property and money can be replaced; your life cannot.

In Cyberspace

Although the Internet is fun, educational, and entertaining, it can also be full of danger if one is not careful. The Internet can be an anonymous medium, which makes it a desirable place for criminals. It can be very difficult to determine a person's identity, description, location, and intention. This is what an Internet predator depends upon to attract his prey and escape untouched.

There are three types of Internet predators that you should be aware of:

UPLOADERS

An uploader is a person who wants to know everything about you, including your first and last name, what you do, where you work, where you live, what school or university you go to, your marital status, and even sexual habits. The main problem with an uploader is that although he may be requesting all of this information from you, he does not share anything about himself. This is a potentially dangerous person.

DOWNLOADERS

A downloader is the exact opposite of an uploader; he will tell you everything about himself and cares little about you. This is usually a person who is seeking consolation from you to make him feel good, and may be a person who has some kind of serious emotional problem that requires professional help. If you are communicating with this type of Internet user, and if he feels that you have not met his needs or disrespected him, he will usually retaliate by sending multiple e-mails containing inappropriate language or threats.

FREELOADERS

A freeloader is a person who will attempt to obtain your password(s) or credit card number(s), so that he can purchase items for free over the net while you get stuck with the bill. This type of Internet predator should be ignored.

If you are currently communicating over the Internet with someone who fits one of the above profiles, you should immediately end your Internet relationship. One way is to simply stop answering e-mails. If this does not work, get a new address or screen name.

• • •

Not everyone you encounter on the Internet will be a "loader." Most will be very pleasant, and just like you, are using the information highway to meet new people and surf cyberspace. Although the Internet is a relatively safe place to visit, you should always remember that any personal information sent electronically can be used to find you, thus making you vulnerable to a crime, be it personal or financial.

On-line relationships are the modern version of the pen pal and a great way to get to know people. There have been many well-publicized marriages that have taken place as a result of on-line relationships. Remember, however, that for every couple that finds True Love on the Internet, there are thousands that do not. Unfortunately, there are some Internet predators that are only interested in one thing—their next victim. Be careful with on-line relationships and what you share with others.

Common sense tempered with caution is still your best protection when it comes to using the Internet. There are a number of common safety tips that you should keep in mind when exploring and communicating on-line:

• Be careful about downloading programs located on the Internet. Some may have viruses that will crash your computer.

• Do not release any personal information when making a purchase or banking (e.g., credit card or chequing/savings account numbers) unless you are absolutely certain of the other person's or company's credibility and connection security. For further information on Internet security, privacy policies, encryption technologies, etc., check the Resources section.

• Keep personal information such as home address or phone number confidential. All family members should be instructed not to release personal information on-line.

• Do not give anyone your Internet account password. No legitimate Internet service provider will send you an e-mail message asking for your password or account information. If you receive such a request, contact your provider immediately.

• Use a nickname and keep your real identity to yourself.

• Disconnect from those who persist in asking for information you do not want to share.

● If someone starts chatting with you about sex, uses inappropriate language, or makes you feel uncomfortable in any other way, end the conversation immediately.

● Do not arrange a personal meeting with anyone you have met on the Internet unless you are able to verify their true identity. If you do decide to meet, do so in a busy public place that is well lit. Also ensure that you arrange your own transportation to and from the meeting and bring a friend or double date. Never meet the person alone. Use the same precautions as you would for meeting a total stranger on the street.

● Report any threats to your Internet provider and the police.

● The Internet is a rapidly evolving medium. Keep current on security issues by periodically referring to websites such as those listed in the Resources section.

Identity Theft

Identity theft occurs when a person you either know, or more likely don't know, steals your credit card numbers, driver's licence number, social insurance number, ATM card number, telephone calling card number, or other key pieces of identification, for the purpose of impersonating you, usually for financial gain. Although victims of this type of crime are usually not saddled with paying the bills racked up by these criminals, they are often left with bad credit reports that may stick with them for months or even years. During this time of credit re-building, a victim of identity theft may have problems writing cheques, obtaining financial loans, renting a home, or even obtaining a job. Often victims of identity theft do not know that they have been victimized until a collection agency calls demanding payment for some merchandise that they never ordered.

Information for identity theft used to be obtained by stealing a person's wallet or purse. Although this is still a common strategy used by these types of criminals, other tactics used by the identity thief include:

DUMPSTER DIVING Thieves often sift through trash cans outside businesses where credit card slips, loan application forms, or credit application forms may be discarded. Unfortunately, many institutions do not shred this written information upon disposal.

MAIL THEFT Credit card bills, cheques, etc. in unsecured mailboxes are primary targets for thieves.

CHANGE OF ADDRESS FRAUD In this scam, the identity thief will fill out a change of address card to divert the intended victim's mail to his drop box.

INSIDER INFORMATION The identity thief, or an accomplice, may be employed in a position in which they have access to employees' personal information, or access to credit reporting bureaus.

● ● ●

So what can you do to help prevent becoming a victim of this increasingly common crime?

● Do not carry extra credit cards, your social insurance card, birth certificate, or passport in your purse unless needed.

● Have your name and address removed from the phone book and reverse directories.

● Install a locked mail box or use a post office box to reduce the chance of mail theft.

● When you order new cheques or credit cards, have them sent to your bank for pickup.

● Keep a list of all credit card numbers, account numbers, and phone numbers for your credit organizations so that you can quickly contact them once you realize that your cards have been stolen.

● Never give your credit card number out over the phone unless you trust the company and have initiated the call.

● Order your credit report once a year from credit bureaus to check for inaccuracies. These phone numbers can be obtained from your local bank.

● Never toss out credit receipts into the trash. Take them with you from the store and ensure they are destroyed by shredding or burning. The same goes for any papers with sensitive or personal information. Also, enquire as to disposal practices of businesses or financial institutions with whom you deal.

● Shield your ATM number or your calling card number from "shoulder surfers" who may be lurking nearby.

● Protect your Social Insurance Number and only give it out when absolutely necessary. If a business asks for your Social Insurance Number, ask why, and see if another number can be used instead.

● Always review all credit card statements and phone and cellular phone bills for any inaccuracies or unauthorized use.

● Ensure that all your active and cancelled cheques are kept in a safe place.

If you are the victim of an identity theft:

● Report the crime to police. Be able to provide them with as much information and documented evidence as possible. Obtain a police case number.

● Call your credit card companies. Report that your credit card(s) have been stolen and request that new cards with new account numbers be issued to you. Document the conversation.

- Advise your bank of the theft. Cancel your chequing and savings accounts and obtain new account numbers. Stop payment on any outstanding cheques.

- If your ATM card is stolen or lost, obtain a new one with a different number and code.

- If you suspect mail theft, notify your local post office official.

- If you have lost your passport notify Immigration Canada and your local police department.

- Call your telephone, electrical, gas, and water companies. Advise them that there is a possibility that someone using your name may attempt to open an account and to contact you or the police if this happens.

- To prevent someone from using your driver's licence number as identification, contact your local motor vehicle branch to obtain a new number and ask them to flag the old one.

- Even if you recover your stolen or lost wallet and the ID is still intact, do not assume the information is secure. Follow procedures as outlined above.

Fraud Crimes

While everyone is a potential victim of fraud, senior citizens are particularly vulnerable. Although seniors often fear that they are prime targets for violent crimes such as assault or robbery, statistically they are the least likely group to be victims of violent crimes in our country. Seniors are more often the victims of financial frauds.

The financial predator knows that many seniors have quick and easy access to large amounts of cash. Many scam artists and organizations specialize in phone, mail, and personal frauds, often taking advantage of seniors who are lonely, confused, trusting, or have poor memories. Such scams often use a woman as the "front man," since people are more likely to trust women.

Everyone, but in particular seniors, should be aware of these frauds and how to prevent them. The following are the most common frauds or con games being used by the financial predator:

THE BANK EXAMINER FRAUD

While sitting at home, you get a call from a professional-sounding person who claims to be a financial officer from your bank. This person shares with you that she is conducting an undercover investigation about the honesty of one of the employees working the cash till, because the bank believes the employee may be skimming money on withdrawals. The "financial officer" then says that she will meet you at your bank and escort you inside so she can watch the teller withdrawing the money. Finally, she will meet you at a predetermined location away from the bank to count the money you received from the teller. To the financial officer's surprise, all the money is there and she thanks you for your co-operation and volunteers to return your money to the bank so that you are not inconvenienced any longer. You hand the money to the thief in good faith, and never see your money again.

THE PIGEON DROP FRAUD

While you are waiting for a bus or while shopping, a person suddenly walks up to you and asks if you have just dropped an envelope that she has miraculously found at your feet. When you say "no," the con artist looks inside the envelope, in which you both see a large amount of cash. The con artist then tells you that she is going to turn this money over to police, and further advises that if the money is not claimed, both you and she can retrieve it after 60 days, at which time you can split it 50/50. As the con walks away, she will suddenly turn, walk back up to you, and then ask you for some collateral (usually half the amount of money in the envelope) to show good faith. Believing that in 60 days not only will you get your collateral back but also half the money in the envelope, and believing that the collateral is a good investment, you freely give the con the money she was looking for in the first place, which is never to be seen again.

TELEMARKETING FRAUD

Telemarketing is big business in Canada, and unfortunately financial predators are using this type of business to swindle hundreds of thousands of dollars from seniors. Always be very careful when dealing with people you do not know over the phone. Although there are a number of legitimate businesses and charities using telemarketing to raise money, there are probably just as many illegitimate companies as well. When conducting business over the phone, never give your credit card information to unsolicited callers, even if they say you have won a "prize" which requires you to pay for shipping or customs duty. Even if the prize is "legitimate," the cost of shipping (or of a 1-900 call) will probably far exceed the value of the item won. Remember, a prize is not a prize if you have to spend any money to get it. As the Better Business Bureau is always reminding us, "If it sounds too good to be true, it probably is."

It is now very easy for financial predators to obtain personal information about you. If you have been conned once, your name and pertinent details will likely be on a computer data base. This data base is bought and sold by these illegitimate companies, with your name flagged as a person who is likely to be conned again.

There are some common words and phrases that should alert you to a potential telemarketing fraud:

- "This is a cash only deal." What's wrong with a cheque?

- "This is such a good deal. Let's keep it our secret because if my boss finds out I could be fired." If it is such a good deal why not tell everyone?

- "You are going to make lots of money very quickly with this deal." How much is it going to cost me first?

- "This deal is good for today only." What is so special about today and why can't it wait until tomorrow?
- "This is your last chance." How many chances have there been?
- "You have just won a free trip to. . . ." How much is it going to cost me?

If you hear these "red flag" phrases, the best thing you can do is to hang up immediately. Before donating money or buying anything unsolicited over the phone, always check with your local Better Business Bureau about the company.

Other fraud schemes that you should be aware of include:

HOME IMPROVEMENT OFFERS The financial predator offers tempting home renovations or improvements at very low prices that must usually be paid up front. The "improvements" rarely take place, or if done, are of low quality. It is usually hopeless to attempt legal action against the ephemeral company.

CHAIN REFERRAL SCHEMES AND OTHER BUSINESS OPPORTUNITIES In chain referral schemes, the financial predator will offer you a commission for buying one item and selling additional ones to friends and families. The products are usually over-priced and difficult to sell. Other business opportunities promise high returns but require a sizeable registration or investment fee.

RETIREMENT ESTATES The financial predator will offer extremely low prices to you, the "lucky" person, on time shares in Florida or other such deals.

MEDICAL FRAUDS Here the financial predator will offer miracle cures for common ailments at high prices.

Combat telemarketing fraud. If you feel a person or business is not being upfront and truthful, contact PROJECT PHONEBUSTERS through your local Better Business Bureau. Project Phonebusters is a joint venture between police, government, the Better Business Bureau, and private enterprises. Give them a call, voice your concerns, and let them investigate.

Travel Safety

Vacation is the time for rest and relaxation and a time when it is easy to let your guard down. It is also a time when you are in unfamiliar surroundings and are therefore more vulnerable. Whether you are travelling for business or pleasure, here are some important safety considerations.

Hotels

Violent crimes against women happen in the best and worst of hotels around the world.

Hotel predators usually play the part of a staff member by dressing and acting like a waiter, security guard, or other hotel employee. The primary way that a predator will gain access to your room is by pushing his way through an open or unlocked door. The second most common way that predators enter hotel rooms is by obtaining a pass key.

Some precautions when staying in any hotel:

● Keep all hotel room doors fully locked, including the patio and adjoining room doors. One of the best ways to secure a hotel room is to kick a wedge under the door when you are inside the room. You may also wish to purchase a door alarm that is designed to go off when a door is opened. These alarms are usually very inexpensive and money well spent for the good night's sleep you will get in return.

● Never open your hotel room door to anyone you do not know until you can identify who they are and why they are there. It is very common for predators to pose as hotel staff wanting to check the room's TV, phone, smoke alarm, or a leaky faucet. Before opening the door, check with the front desk.

● If someone knocks on your door and then says "I'm sorry, I've got the wrong room," contact the front desk immediately. Most people know what room they, or friends, are in. A person who uses this tactic is checking occupancy of the room. If no one answers, then the predator may break in.

● When leaving your hotel room, leave a TV on and the "Do Not Disturb" sign hanging on the door to make your room look occupied. If you need your room cleaned, call the cleaning staff and stay in the room with them until it's done.

● When out of your room, do not leave tempting valuables such as jewellery, money, credit cards, passports, plane tickets, camera equipment, and calling cards lying around. If you have valuables with you, keep them in the hotel safe or a "portable safe." These come in many forms such as hollow books, suitcases with secret compartments, fake pop cans, etc.

● When checking into or out of a hotel, always have your luggage in sight. What can't be seen by you, can be taken by a thief.

● Plan ahead. Have maps and specific directions before you reach your destination. Make your hotel reservations in advance and secure them with your credit card. Otherwise, if area hotels are booked up, you may find yourself stranded. Let your friends or family know your travel plans and course of travel.

● If your room is not ready, and you have to go out, ask to have your luggage stored in a locked room. Many hotels have a "day room" where you can put your luggage and freshen up.

● When completing the guest registry, sign your name gender neutral, using only your first initial and last name.

● If you can, register with your business address instead of your home address.

● Advise the front desk never to release your room number to anyone without checking with you first.

● If the hotel has more than one building, request a room in or near the main building. If you can, request a room between the second and seventh floors and near a fire exit if possible. This will allow you to be high enough so access to windows is difficult, but it will also allow you a quick and easy exit in an emergency. There are more than 6,000 hotel fires in the USA every year. In 1992, hotel fires caused 30 deaths and 250 injuries. Therefore, be sure to review the fire instructions provided by the hotel. As soon as you check in, find out where the nearest fire exit is, and how many doors it is away from your room, should the hallways be filled with smoke. Most hotel room doors automatically lock when shut. Always take your room key with you if attempting escape in smoky hallways. If your exit is barred by fire, at least you can get back into your room. If your room door feels hot, do not open it. Fill the bathtub with water and soak yourself in it. Hold a wet towel or cloth to your nose and mouth to prevent breathing in smoke, and block the bottom of the room door with wet material.

● Keep away from rooms next to elevators, ice machines, vending machines, basements, garbage rooms, and rooms immediately adjacent to stairwells. These are areas where predators may wait for an opportunity to arise and areas which allow for easy exit.

● Request a key that does not have your room number on it in case the key is lost or stolen.

● Do not park your car in a stall that has your room number on it. If you pull away from the stall, a predator watching knows that your room is now probably vacant.

● Ask the front desk staff about the safest areas for jogging, walking, shopping, etc. Ask for a map of the area you are staying in. If you are going out for the evening, ask if taxis or public transit stop running at a certain hour. Also ask them if there is anything else that you should be aware of such as common "con games" used on tourists.

Airports and Baggage

Airports are a favorite venue for thieves and con artists. Some of these criminals work in packs to confuse both you and the authorities. Their primary tactic is the use of a DISTRACTION TECHNIQUE which will allow them to relieve you of your personal belongings, such as your luggage, purse, wallet, backpack, laptop, or any other articles you may have with you. Common scams are described below. Your only defences against these are to be aware of them, so that you can recognize them when they happen, and to pay close attention to your belongings at all times.

THE "IS THIS YOUR MONEY?" DISTRACTION

A well-dressed man or woman will approach you and say, "Excuse me, I think you dropped some money on the floor." As you look down, you do in fact see some money (that the predator has thrown) and as you reach for it, the predator snatches your suitcase and you are none the wiser. It is often only later, when you are ready to catch your plane, that you realize your bag is gone.

THE KETCHUP OR MUSTARD SQUIRT DISTRACTION

This is probably the most popular distraction technique being used in airports around the world. Here the predator will poke a hole in a small package of ketchup or mustard and squirt some of the contents onto you without your knowledge. The predator will then bring this to your attention, and, as you are cleaning yourself up, he makes off with your personal items.

THE ESCALATOR DISTRACTION

As you are using an airport escalator, you notice a person at the top in some sort of distress. As you get closer to this person, you move to one side of the escalator to get out of the way. As you are doing this, so are the other two or more accomplices who are working with this "person in distress," and have now bunched up behind you. With your attention diverted, the accomplices now have a good opportunity to steal your bags.

THE "OH, POOR THING" DISTRACTION

As you are waiting for your plane, a small child will approach you and feign injury or say he is lost. As you are trying to help, the predator moves in. Predators understand that children seem innocent and use this fact to their advantage.

THE BATHROOM DISTRACTION

Predators often target bathrooms, and sit in a stall until a person enters one next to them. While you are occupied, the predator will reach under or over the stall to take your purse that is hanging on the door hook or sitting on the floor. The best place to put your belongings is on the tank behind you, or on your lap if there is no tank.

THE X-RAY DISTRACTION

In this distraction technique, two predators who have bought plane tickets will scan the airport for potential victims carrying laptop computers or other expensive belongings. As you head towards the security check-in point, where you have to send your carry-on luggage through the X-ray conveyer belt, the two predators will very discreetly walk ahead of you. The first predator walks through the security station without any problem. The second predator will approach the gate, hesitate just long enough for you to place your laptop on the conveyer belt, and then he will walk through security wearing items that will set off the metal detector alarm, or stall by means of some other distraction (such as searching for his boarding pass). While you are delayed in this fashion, your laptop is riding on the conveyer belt to the other side, where the first predator takes it and makes a clean getaway. This distraction technique is becoming very popular with thieves in airports around the world.

In addition to the above distraction techniques, you should realize that you are vulnerable to theft whenever your attention is elsewhere—while you are distracted by reading a departure or arrival sign; while watching a luggage carousel; while using a pay phone (remember to always stand so that the phone is at your back); or while signing for a rental car.

Finally, here are some tips to help keep your luggage safe:

● Carry valuables on your person, not in your luggage. Use a money belt, particularly for passports, plane tickets, and travellers' cheques.

● If your carry-on luggage is going through an X-ray machine, make sure you go through security first so that you are at the end of the machine's conveyer belt as it passes through.

● Lock your luggage or wrap it with cord or tape to prevent theft by airport baggage staff.

● Luggage tags that have your personal information on them should be placed face down in their sleeves. If possible, use your business address.

● Avoid expensive luggage. Dishonest baggage handlers may assume it has valuables inside.

● Make your luggage distinctive so that another well-meaning traveller will not accidentally take the wrong pieces.

● If your luggage is lost or stolen, report it and fill out a certificate of loss immediately.

● If you have several pieces of luggage, and have a long layover in the terminal, use a coin-operated locker to store everything.

● Be extremely careful about accepting offers of assistance from anyone other than identified carrier station personnel.

Rental Cars

Another important safety consideration for travellers is the use of rental cars. There have been a number of well-publicized incidents in which predators have waited outside of airports, train stations, bus depots, and cruise line docks for travellers using rental vehicles. If you are going to be renting a car, here are some safety tips that you may want to consider:

● Do not rent a vehicle that displays the name of the rental company anywhere on it, including the licence plate. To do so is advertising that you are from out of town and therefore an easy target to prey upon.

● Do not leave anything of value inside the rental vehicle. Predators know that the courts will not likely bring victims of thefts back for trial due to the costs associated with travel, meals, and accommodations.

● Do not have maps out in plain view. If you have touristy items such as luggage or garment bags, place them in the trunk.

● If you have car problems stay in your vehicle. There is no better safety device than having a cell phone with you. Most car rental companies now offer clients pre-programmed 9-1-1 cell phones as well as emergency roadside service. Take full advantage of any safety options offered.

● Before taking your rental car out, walk around it first and look for problems that might stop you on the road, such as low tire pressure or a hanging muffler. If you see a problem, request a new car.

Travelling Abroad

Before visiting any foreign country, it is important that you familiarize yourself with your destination. There may be cultural differences that you should be aware of; for example, men in some other countries are much more verbally and physically aggressive towards women than in Canada. Also, codes of dress vary, and you may wish to adapt to these customs to blend in, thus being less of a target and more comfortable. Because safety concerns vary widely in different countries, this section is by no means a complete treatment of safety while abroad. However, here are some general tips to follow before you leave the country:

• Contact your travel agency and automobile association for information, including passport, visa, and immunization requirements.

• Inform yourself as thoroughly as possible about safety issues by consulting books, the Internet, and other travellers who have been to your destination.

• If you take prescription drugs, bring enough with you to cover your stay. To make customs processing easier and to avoid violating drug laws of the country you are visiting, leave all medications in their labelled containers, and have a copy of your doctor's prescription.

• Become familiar with the laws of the country. Know the address and phone number of the nearest Canadian Embassy.

• Learn key words and phrases ("police", "doctor", "emergency", "I need help") in the country's language. Carry a small dictionary or phrase book.

• Learn how to use the phone system. For example, in some cities, you may have trouble finding payphones that accept coins.

• Treat your passport and plane tickets like gold. Always carry your passport with you, but separate from other items such as your wallet. There are a variety of money holders on the market (calf belts, bra pouches, etc.) and it is absolutely essential that you invest in at least one of these. Plane tickets should be kept in your hotel's safe. Make copies of all credit cards, IDs, passports, and personal papers you are taking and keep these separate from the originals.

• Keep a low profile and don't flaunt valuables that draw attention to yourself.

• Avoid carrying large amounts of cash at any one time. Use travellers' cheques, and record their numbers. Take only one credit card and record its number as well.

• If you can, travel or sightsee with another person. Criminals abroad, as in Canada, rarely target two or more people. However, women travelling together may still be vulnerable. Two young female friends of ours were the victims of an attempted robbery on a night train in Italy, in which the criminal placed barbiturates in apparently sealed juice containers. (They were lucky; he was caught and they recovered from the poisoning.) Inform yourself about the latest such scams being perpetrated on tourists abroad.

● Keep in touch with your family or friends back home. Let them know that you are okay. And have a great trip!

CHAPTER FIVE

Stalking and Sexual Assaults

Stalking and Criminal Harassment

What is Criminal Harassment?

Although "stalking" is a well-recognized term in Canada, the correct legal name is "Criminal Harassment." If you fear for your physical or emotional safety because someone is:

- threatening you or a loved one
- following or continually watching you or a loved one
- threatening your pets
- damaging your personal property
- continually sending things that you do not want
- continually calling you, family, friends, or co-workers and asking about you

and as a result of these actions you are fearful and feel inhibited in following your normal routine, this may be Criminal Harassment.

Criminal harassers may have a variety of motivations: jealousy, anger over a perceived or real injustice, the desire to intimidate, romantic obsession. Stalking, however, has nothing to do with love and respect and everything to do with power and control. A stalker can be anyone, but patterns do emerge. A study conducted in 1996 by the RCMP, the Vancouver Police Department, and the Attorney General found the following:

- 101 people were charged with Criminal Harassment in Greater Vancouver
- of the 101 charged, 89 were male and 12 were female
- of the women, half stalked men
- of the men, 79 (or 88%) stalked women
- 71% of the victims were ex-partners
- 14% were friends/family
- 9% were strangers
- 6% were clients, patients, or former co-workers

Canadian Criminal Code

Section 264(1) of the Criminal Code of Canada states the following:

> No person shall, without lawful authority and knowing that another person is harassed or recklessly as to whether the other person is harassed, engage in conduct referred to in subsection (2) that causes that other person reasonably, in all circumstances, to fear for their safety or the safety of anyone known to them.

the conduct mentioned in subsection (1) consists of

a) repeatedly following from place to place the other person or anyone known to them;

b) repeatedly communicating with, either directly or indirectly, the other person or anyone known to them;

c) besetting or watching the dwelling-house, or place where the other person, or anyone known to them, resides, works, carries on business or happens to be; or

d) engaging in threatening conduct directed at the other person or any member of their family.

Every person who contravenes this section is guilty of

a) an indictable offence and is liable to imprisonment for a term not exceeding five years; or

b) an offence punishable on summary conviction.

If the police cannot prove a Criminal Harassment has taken place, there are other criminal code sections that they might be able to act upon, such as:

- Section 177: Trespass By Night
- Section 264: Utter Threats
- Section 372: Indecent and Harassing Telephone Calls
- Section 423: Intimidation
- Section 430: Mischief

What You Can Do

What should you do if you believe that you are the victim of Criminal Harassment?

NOTIFY THE AUTHORITIES

In 98% of the cases, once police are involved, the criminal harassment will stop. The police will ask you to complete a written statement in which it is essential that you are thorough and honest. If the police have reasonable grounds to believe that there is a Criminal Harassment violation, an arrest can be made. The person charged with this serious offence will then appear before a judge and, if not remanded in custody until his or her court date, will be released under a court order not to have any contact with you, your friends, family members, or co-workers either directly or indirectly. If the person charged with this offence violates any of these conditions, he can be arrested for breaching a court order, held in custody, and placed in front of the courts on the new charge.

KEEP A WRITTEN RECORD

The more information that you, a family member, friend, or co-worker can record about the who, what, where, when, why, and how of the harassment, the better. It is very important for police documentation and investigation that you record the dates and times of these contacts and any witnesses who may have been present. A harasser often leaves messages on your answering machine, e-mail messages, notes, gifts, etc. Keep them as they are important pieces of evidence.

TAKE PRECAUTIONS

- Inform people you know and trust about what is going on and what they can do to help.

- Avoid frequenting locations where you are likely to encounter the harasser.

- Never agree to meet with the harasser. Often, women believe that they can work things out by having a rational conversation with the offender. You *cannot* change this person's mind, and trying to do so may only place you in a dangerous situation.

Criminal Harassment is a life-changing experience that nobody should ever have to endure. Stalkers destroy their victims' feelings of safety, security, emotional stability, and even self-worth, if the victim feels she is somehow to blame.

You have the right to be heard and helped when it comes to dealing with Criminal Harassment. Go to the police, and seek help from other organizations including your local Victim Services office, Sexual Assault Centre, or Women's Transition House.

Sexual Assault

What is Sexual Assault?

Sexual assault involves any unwanted sexual touching, ranging from breast fondling to forced intercourse with serious injuries and even death. Consent is a key issue in determining whether a sexual assault has taken place. According to the Criminal Code of Canada, a person cannot consent to sexual activity if impaired by alcohol or drugs. Also, consent must be clearly and freely given; i.e., a definite "yes," and not under psychological or emotional duress. Legal consent cannot be given by anyone under 14 years of age (not 16, as many people mistakenly believe).

The statistics regarding this crime in Canada are startling:

- 50% of females in Canada have been victims of one or more unwanted sexual acts.
- Almost 60% of women who experienced a sexual assault were the targets of more than one such incident.
- A woman is sexually assaulted every 6 minutes in Canada, and every 7 minutes involving forced sexual intercourse.
- Survivors of sexual assault range in age from 4 months to over 90 years.
- The largest target group is young women aged 14–24 years.
- 49% of all sexual assaults occur in broad daylight.
- The number one place where sexual assaults occur is in the home. The number two place is in a vehicle.
- 25% of all sexual assaults involving forced intercourse occur after the offender has made a "legitimate" contact with the woman.
- 83% of all sexual assaults on women are committed by a male they know.
- 50% of incidents involve couples either married or cohabiting at the time of the assault.
- 99% of sexual offenders are male.
- Sexual offenders overwhelmingly represent the "average" male. The vast majority of men who sexually assault women in Canada are white (72%) and Canadian-born (63%).
- Only about 10% of sexual assaults are reported to police.
- Only 1% of women who have been assaulted by an acquaintance report the crime to police.

Sexual Assault Myths

One possible factor contributing to the high incidence of sexual assault may be the many myths that surround the issue. These myths are still believed by a large proportion of the population, including women. Each time we teach and lecture, we are amazed that these fallacies never seem to die. They have to be recognized for what they are, *lies,* and need to be dealt with as such. They include:

- The way a woman looks, dresses, or acts can promote a sexual assault ("flaunting it,""asking for it").
- A woman's reputation can promote a sexual assault.
- Some women like to or want to be assaulted and therefore deserve to be.
- Some women or some situations are safe.
- Women must accept a certain amount of risk when they participate in certain activities, i.e., going to bars.
- Women, and especially those who are young, elderly, or disabled, are incapable of protecting themselves and resisting an assault.
- An assailant will always cause more injury if the woman resists him.
- Most women are lucky if they successfully defend themselves and get away.
- Resisting an assailant who has a weapon will result in certain death.
- A woman can tell who her attacker may be by the way the attacker looks.
- Men cannot control themselves sexually in certain situations.
- Assaults are usually committed by strangers.
- Some assaults should be taken more seriously than others.
- Women often cry rape to get even with men or to protect their reputations.
- If a woman is kissing or consenting to some physical touching, it means that she is willing to have sexual intercourse.
- A woman should be able to see a sexual assault coming and should know better than to place herself in that type of situation, or to "lead a man on."

- A woman should never go out alone after dark because if she does, she is just asking for trouble.
- Sexual assault is a crime of passion and lust.
- You cannot be sexually assaulted against your will.
- A person who has been sexually assaulted will be hysterical.
- Sexual assault is an impulsive act.
- Only young, pretty women are sexually assaulted.
- If you do not use physical force to resist an attack, then you have not been sexually assaulted.
- All rapists are crazy and sexually frustrated.

Remember, a sexual assault, no matter what the circumstance, is *never* the victim's fault. Examine your own attitudes about this crime, and help destroy these all-too-common myths. Speak out. Insist that perpetrators be held responsible for their actions, and join initiatives aimed at reducing violence against women and violence in society in general.

Acquaintance or "Date" Rape

Rape is Rape

The sad reality is that if you are going to be sexually assaulted, your attacker will probably be someone you know, love, or trust. In fact, 83% of men who sexually assault women are known to their victims.

Acquaintance rape is a very real problem for women of all ages, but especially those between the ages of 14 and 24. Only 1% of women who have experienced acquaintance rape actually report the crime to police. Acquaintance rape is a real concern for women in today's world, yet there is a sore lack of attention to education and prevention on this matter.

What is date rape? Our definition of date rape is any unwanted sexual contact between you and a person you know. Sexual assault is an act of violence, and it can take place with someone you just met, someone you have been dating, or with someone to whom you are engaged or married. Remember, rape is rape. Date rape is every bit as serious an offence as any other type of sexual assault.

Why is date rape such a problem? Socialization has a large part to play. If you consider traditional male and female roles, men have always been taught to be aggressors, to get what they want, and not to give up until they have attained their goals. They have been encouraged to experiment with their sexuality because that is "part of being a man."

Women, on the other hand, have been socially conditioned to be passive and dependent, to avoid scenes, and to always be "lady-like." Women are discouraged from experimenting with sex. "Good girls" do not fool around or talk about sex; only sluts do. The closest male equivalents for the word "slut" (playboy, philanderer, roué) do not have nearly the same negative connotations!

Studies have also indicated that miscommunication is a factor. There has been a gradual loosening of sexual standards over the past few decades. In the 90s, it is not unusual for people seeing one another to have consensual sex after just a few dates, behaviour which was unheard of not so long ago. Because of these loosening standards, some men have come to expect sex after only a few dates, while many women may not. It is important that couples communicate honestly and frankly about sex and each other's expectations at an early stage in the dating process. Unfortunately, this type of communication is not taught to our young people early enough to be natural and acceptable.

Finally, perhaps the most important factor contributing to date rape is that some men need the power and control that comes with raping women. These men are sexually aggressive because they are insecure with their masculinity. They rape to make themselves feel strong by making someone else feel weak.

The Scary Facts

One in four young women will be sexually assaulted before the age of 18. When grade school students in the U.S. were surveyed about sexual assault, the following statistics were revealed:

- 56% of the girls and 76% of the boys believed that forced sex was acceptable under some circumstances.
- In the 11–14 age bracket, 51% of boys and 41% of girls said that forced sex was acceptable if the boy "spent a lot of money" on the girl.
- 31% of the boys and 32% of the girls said that it was acceptable for a man to rape a woman if she had past sexual experience.
- 87% of the boys and 79% of the girls believed that sexual assault was acceptable if the man and the woman were married.
- 65% of the boys and 47% of the girls stated that it was acceptable for a boy to rape a girl if they had been dating for more than six months.

A survey of over 6,000 college students enrolled at 32 colleges in the United States revealed the following:

- One in four women in college had been a survivor of a rape or attempted rape by someone they knew.
- 57% of sexual assaults took place while on a date.
- 73% of the assailants and 55% of the survivors had used alcohol or drugs prior to the assault.
- 42% percent of survivors told no one.
- 35% percent of college males admitted that under certain circumstances, they would commit rape if they believed that they could get away with it.

• One in twelve male college students admitted to committing acts that met the legal definition of rape, and 84% of those men who committed rape did not label it as rape.

• 43% percent of college men admitted to using coercive behaviour to have sex, including ignoring a woman's protest and using physical aggression to force intercourse.

• 15% acknowledged they had committed date rape, and 11% acknowledged using physical restraints to force a woman to have sex.

Although there is no single date rape scenario, a study conducted by the Association of American Colleges in 1987 found the following generalities:

• Most date rapes occur when the woman is alone with a man in a home, apartment, car, etc.

• Alcohol and drugs are sometimes factors in date rape scenarios. Either the victim is too drunk to realize what is going on, or the male has drunk too much and uses it as an excuse to become sexually active.

• "Mixed signals" are perceived by the man. He interprets friendliness incorrectly; hears "No" as "Yes," especially if it is said mildly; interprets enjoyment of kissing and caressing to mean that the woman wants to have sex, and feels cheated or "led on" if she then refuses.

• Most date rapes are spontaneous but some are planned in advance.

• The men have usually done it before and have gotten away with it in the past.

• Date rapists usually look for women who are unassertive and not popular.

Avoidance Strategies

Although date rape is not 100% preventable, the more you know about it, the better able you are to avoid it. Remember that while we suggest ways to help women avoid date rape, if it does happen, rape in any form is *never* the victim's fault.

The Association of American Colleges suggests the following avoidance strategies:

● Examine your feelings about sex.

- Set sexual limits; it's your body and no one has the right to make you do anything that you do not want to do. If you do not want someone to touch you in a specific way, say so and mean it.

- Decide early on in the relationship if you would like to have sex. The sooner you communicate with your partner about your sexual limits, the easier it will be for him to accept your decision.

- Do not give mixed messages—say "Yes" when you mean it, and say "No" when you mean it. Be forceful and firm. Men may interpret passivity as permission to carry on doing what they are doing. If the man continues on with his actions after you have said no, say, "Stop, this is rape."

- Be independent and aware on your date. For example, especially when starting to date someone, pay your own way.

- Do not do anything you do not want to do just to avoid a scene or unpleasantness, or to avoid hurting his feelings—after all, he is ignoring yours.

- Be aware of specific situations in which you do not feel relaxed or in charge. Being "paranoid" is better than being raped. Acknowledge a dangerous situation for what it is. Avoid situations in which men far outnumber women.

- If things get out of hand, be loud in protesting, leave, and go for help. Do not wait for someone else to rescue you.

- Trust your gut instinct. If you feel you are being pressured, you probably are. If you feel uncomfortable, leave.

- Be aware that alcohol and drugs are often related to date rape. Do not compromise your ability to make responsible decisions.

- If you are unsure about a new acquaintance, go on a group or double date. If this is not possible meet in a public place.

- Have your own transportation home or taxi fare, especially on the first few dates.

- Be careful when you invite someone to your home or you are invited to his home. These are the two most likely places where date rapes occur.

The Association of American Colleges also found that there are certain traits that make men more likely to be sexually aggressive towards women. The following are red flags that you should watch out for:

- men who do not listen to you or ignore what you have to say
- men who ignore your personal space or boundaries
- men who express anger or aggression towards women as individuals or in general
- men who do what they want regardless of what you want
- men who try to make you feel guilty or accuse you of being uptight
- men who are excessively jealous or possessive
- men who have wrong or unrealistic ideas about women's roles in society
- men who drink heavily

There are also a number of come-on lines that are often used by the date rapist and that one should be aware of:

- Pressure for Sex Lines:
  - "If you loved me you would."
  - "You are not the only girl I could date."

- Trying to Make You Feel Bad or Guilt Lines:
  - "Don't you like me? Because if you did, you would."
  - "Are you weird or something? Everyone else is doing it."

- Blackmail Lines:
  - "I will kill myself if you break up with me."
  - "If you don't, I will tell everyone you did it anyway."

- Thinks Sex is His Right No Matter What Lines:
  - "You have turned me on, now you have to finish what you started."
  - "We had sex before, so you can't say no now."

- Doesn't Take No for an Answer Lines:
  - "You can't say no because I just spent all that money on you."
  - "You really want it. You are just saying no to protect your reputation."

If you do find yourself in a date rape situation, there are a number of things that you should remember. First, remain calm. If you panic, you are his for the taking. You need to say "NO" strongly and mean it. Don't smile, don't act friendly, and don't be polite.

Tell him that if he does not stop what he is doing it will be rape. If you can, look for an escape route. Negotiating skills (including fake pleasantness) may be effective to buy you time to get out of the situation. You also need to act as soon as possible. The longer the date rape continues, the harder it is going to be to escape. If you do decide to fight back, your goal is to stun and run. Again, study after study has found that women who physically resist sexual assaults survive with less physical and mental trauma.

The Survivor

Every woman will react differently to being raped. In date rape, although the person who rapes you is someone you know, the trauma that you experience is often more intense than if you had been raped by a stranger. Your feelings of trust, both in another human being and in yourself, have been totally betrayed.

Many survivors of date rape fear that if they tell someone what happened they will not be believed. Others, through disassociation or denial, may not even identify the sexual assault as a rape. The survivor may also not wish to admit to being sexually assaulted because she was drinking or using drugs. All these reasons, and many more, often mean that the survivor does not ask for the support or counselling she now needs.

The survivor may suffer sleeplessness, nightmares, poor concentration, anxiety, loss of appetite, loss of self-confidence, stress-related illness, grief, and despair. Often many survivors become depressed and withdrawn, experiencing fear and a generalized loss of trust. If the survivor is a student, she may transfer to another school or drop out of school altogether.

It is not unusual for the survivor to begin to blame herself for what has happened. Why did I accept a ride from him? ... I should not have gone to that party. ... I should never have gone into his apartment. ... Why did I let him kiss me? ... How could I have been so stupid? It is important to understand that the person who raped you is at fault. The rapist is the person who committed the crime and not you. Alcohol and drugs, whether used by you or the rapist, do not excuse the rapist's behaviour.

Earlier we stated that fewer than 1% of women who have been assaulted by a date or acquaintance actually report the crime to police. Predators who commit these types of sexual assaults have one of the highest recidivism rates of any crime. Why? Because the survivors do not report the crime to the authorities. The predator knows there is a very strong likelihood he will not be caught and therefore may continue to victimize others. By reporting this crime, you are taking control back from the predator and saying to him that what he has done to you is criminal, and he will not get away with it this time, or ever again.

Sexual Assault Drugs

For centuries, sexual predators have used a wide variety of substances to sedate and sexually exploit women. These have included herbs, alcohol, common cold pills, sedatives, and illegal narcotics. Recently, because of a number of highly publicized sexual assaults in both the United States and Canada, sexual assault drugs have come to the attention of law enforcement agencies. Two insidious sexual assault drugs which women should be aware of are Gamma Hydroxybutyrate (GHB) and Rohypnol. The use of both of these drugs is on the rise.

Most hospital drug screening tests do not routinely check for GHB and Rohypnol. Therefore, if you believe you have been sexually assaulted while drugged, it is important that you bring this to the attention of the hospital medical staff so that the appropriate tests can be carried out. If you cannot get to a hospital immediately, police recommend taking a urine sample and storing it in the fridge since these drugs pass through the system rapidly.

Gamma Hydroxybutyrate (GHB)

GHB is a central nervous system depressant that has been prescribed by doctors to treat some sleep disorders as well as alcoholism. During the 1980s, GHB was believed to stimulate certain human growth hormones and as such, became popular with athletes and bodybuilders. Recently GHB has once again emerged, this time as a recreational drug known as "Liquid Ecstasy," offering a high similar to alcohol intoxication but without the hangover. Even though GHB is now a banned substance, it is still readily available, as it is easily made with common ingredients. Its use has increased, probably due to Internet sites that give information on how to make the drug. Some sites also sell kits for making the drug (often marketed for its supposed health benefits). Some products sold in health food stores and on the Internet (including Firewater, Blue Nitro Vitality, Revivarant, RenewTrient) contain GBL (gamma butyrolactone), which is metabolized by the body into GHB. These products have caused a number of deaths in the U.S.

In low dosages, GHB may cause amnesia, hypnotic events, drowsiness, uninhibited behaviour, or impaired judgement.

In higher doses, the victim may experience a slow heart rate, seizure-like activity, breathing difficulties, loss of consciousness, or may even slip into a coma. If GHB is mixed with alcohol these effects can become even more severe. In liquid form, concentrated GHB may appear thicker than water and usually has a very salty taste. When mixed with a drink, however, GHB is so diluted (only 2–3 drops needed) that it is tasteless as well as colourless and odourless.

GHB will usually take effect about 15–30 minutes after ingestion, producing a high for one to three hours. After this, the victim has no short-term recall of the preceding events. Detection of GHB is possible but extremely difficult, as it is only traceable in the blood two to four hours after ingestion. It is also found in the urine, but all traces of the drug often leave the body with the first urination. Not surprisingly, police have difficulty laying charges in such cases for this reason.

Rohypnol ("Roofies")

Rohypnol, the trade name for flunitrazepam, is used as sleeping medication in over 60 countries around the world, but is not approved in Canada and the United States. Rohypnol is usually distributed in little white tablets that contain the name "Roche" and an encircled "1" or "2" on one side, with a single or cross score on the other. Much like GHB, when dissolved in a liquid, it is tasteless and odourless and cannot be detected visually. Concerned about the illicit use of their product, the manufacturers of Rohypnol have added a dye that will turn a liquid blue as an early warning system. In the future, they hope to change the tablet so that it will not dissolve in liquid.

Symptoms of Rohypnol intoxication include: impaired judgement, impaired motor skills, loss of inhibitions, amnesia, drowsiness, dizziness, confusion, and in some people, excitability. If too much is ingested, coma or death may result.

When Rohypnol is mixed with alcohol, it offers a cheap and long-lasting high in which intoxication effects are enhanced. Although the drug is not legally available in Canada, it can be readily obtained by sexual predators. Very recently, over 5000 packages of Rohypnol were seized in a raid on a drug house in Vancouver.

If ingested, Rohypnol can be detected in the urine for up to 72 hours, but only for a few hours in the blood. A 2 mg dose (1 pill) can incapacitate an average female for between eight and twelve hours, after which she will usually have no memory about what has taken place.

Prevention Strategies

There are a number of steps you can take to reduce the risk of becoming a victim of these types of drugs.

● When in a bar or out partying, keep your drink with you at all times.

● Be careful when accepting drinks from anyone other than bar staff. (Remember, you are most likely to be sexually assaulted by someone you know.) Very recently, a woman at a nightclub in Victoria was given a shooter by a new acquaintance. This was the last thing she remembered when she woke up, nude, in a strange hotel room.

● Do not accept open-container drinks at parties.

● When at a party, mix your own drinks.

● If a friend seems drunk, but has not had enough alcohol to warrant this level of intoxication, pay attention to her, and do not let her leave with anyone other than you. If symptoms are serious, take her to emergency immediately.

Domestic Violence and Assault

What is Domestic Violence?

Mention "domestic violence," and most people imagine a husband and wife getting into a verbal argument which then leads to a physical brawl. Domestic violence actually encompasses a much broader scope of abuse which can involve physical violence. It occurs whenever a spouse, common law partner, or a date uses physical violence, threats, emotional abuse, harassment, or stalking to *control* and *dominate* the behaviour of their partner.

Domestic violence can happen to anyone and crosses all ethnic, racial, age, religious, and socio-economic lines. It can happen in homosexual as well as heterosexual relationships. Victims of domestic violence may be doctors, business professionals, judges, and scientists. The abusers have included sports heroes, police officers, lawyers, CEOs, and Members of Parliament. There are, however, two traits common to those who commit domestic violence: most witnessed domestic violence in their family when they were younger; and most are male.

Commonly, victims of domestic violence don't identify themselves as such, and often remain silent from a sense of personal shame and embarrassment and a fear of disapproval from family, friends, and co-workers. Many victims of domestic violence also fear retaliation from their abuser if they tell others about the violence. Often both the victim and the abuser will minimize their actions and characterize the abuse as a "family quarrel" that got out of hand.

Physical abuse is most often conducted in a systematic pattern. The circle of violence, or battering cycle, is recognized by its three distinct stages—a tension build-up period, the physical assault, and finally the "honeymoon" stage. In this last stage, the abuser promises never to do it again, and showers his partner with affection in a manner truly believable to his victim. However, the physical assaults do not end, but become more frequent and often more intense.

According to Statistics Canada (1996):

- 89% of all spousal assaults reported to the police involved a female victim.

• Most incidents of domestic violence involved couples between the ages of 18 and 24, living in common law relationships, and experiencing long-term unemployment of the male partner.

• Spousal killings were often preceded by a history of domestic violence.

• One-quarter of family homicides involving children and seniors took place in families with a known domestic violence history.

• 21% of women abused by a current or previous partner were assaulted while pregnant.

• One in five women assaulted by a former partner were assaulted during a separation or after they separated from their partner. In one-third of cases, the violence increased at the time of separation.

• In 43% of all domestic assaults, the female partner required medical attention.

• At least one Canadian woman in four (2.6 million women per year) experienced physical abuse by a present or past male partner.

Myths about Domestic Violence

There are a number of myths and misperceptions about domestic violence that need to be put to rest.

Victims of domestic violence like to be beaten.

No one wants to be assaulted. Many victims are looking for a way out but do not know how. Some battered partners deny or minimize the physical abuse as a coping strategy to reduce its psychological impact.

Victims of domestic violence must have psychological disorders if they remain in abusive relationships.

The only psychological disorder most victims of domestic violence have is post-traumatic stress as a direct result of the abuse. In early stages of the battering, the victim sincerely hopes that her partner will change his abusive ways and that the battering will stop.

Low self-esteem causes victims to get involved in abusive relationships.

There are no scientific studies that show that low self-esteem is in any way related to a person's risk of becoming a victim of domestic violence.

Victims of domestic abuse never leave their abusers, or if they do, they just get involved in another abusive relationship.

It is often extremely difficult for the person to leave a domestic situation for a variety of reasons such as financial concerns and children. Additionally, a perceived lack of support from others including the police, courts, friends, family, and co-workers may cause victims to stay in abusive relationships. There is no reason to assume that women who leave an abusive relationship will get themselves involved in another.

Domestic violence is a result of alcohol or drug abuse.

Excessive and continuous use of drugs and alcohol may contribute to the frequency or severity of a violent episode, but it is never the root cause. The sole responsibility lies with the abuser.

The police and the courts cannot help the victims of domestic violence.

When the police and the courts become involved in domestic violence incidents, the circle of violence often breaks. If they are not involved, the abuse will almost certainly continue.

Warning Signs

Many studies have now identified a number of characteristic behaviours exhibited by people who are prone to domestic violence. Most of these are based upon the need for power and control over another person. This list, although not exhaustive, can help you or someone you know recognize a potentially dangerous situation.

In an abusive relationship, the partner may:
- use destructive criticism/verbal abuse
- use pressure tactics against you
- constantly abuse authority
- be disrespectful
- abuse trust
- constantly break promises
- withhold emotionally
- minimize situations, deny responsibility, and blame others
- have full economic control
- show self-destructive behaviour
- keep you isolated from friends and family
- be extremely jealous

- harass and stalk you
- physically intimidate you
- destroy possessions of yours
- threaten to hurt you or a loved one or pet
- use sexual violence
- use physical violence
- use or threaten to use a weapon
- threaten to use children in a separation

The Law

In Canada, domestic violence is a crime. A person who commits this type of violence can be charged under a variety of sections of the Criminal Code of Canada including Assault, Sexual Assault, Threatening, and Criminal Harassment. Once police are involved, it becomes the responsibility of the police and Crown Counsel, and not the victim, to proceed with charges against the batterer.

It is also important to understand that if the authorities are not called at the time of the assault, a woman has the right to report it at a later time to the police, who then have a duty to investigate. Although reporting an assault that has happened in the past is acceptable, sooner is always better for your own protection.

If the police and Crown Counsel feel that there is not enough evidence to proceed with charges, a victim may still make application to a criminal court of law, to have a peace bond/restraining order placed against her abuser. This peace bond/restraining order is a court order which places restrictions on the abuser, such as forbidding contact with you or other persons directly or indirectly; staying outside of a certain distance of your residence, workplace, or other places; and other restrictions specific to your case. If an abuser breaches a peace bond/restraining order, he can be arrested. For more information about peace bonds/restraining orders, contact your local police department, Women's Transition House, legal aid services, or Victim Services organization in your community.

Getting Out of an Abusive Relationship

The first and most important thing you can do is to acknowledge that you are in a dangerous situation. Once you have accepted this fact, you can now take certain steps to ensure your safety.

- **If at home and being threatened or attacked**:

  - Call 9-1-1 immediately.
  - Stay away from the kitchen, where there are many weapons such as knives and heavy pans.
  - Stay away from small rooms or spaces where your abuser can trap you.
  - Get out of the home, if possible, and go to a trusted neighbour's or friend's place to call for help.
  - Yell for help even if your attacker tells you to stay quiet. Many potentially deadly domestic disputes have been interrupted by police who attended when neighbours heard trouble and called 9-1-1.

- **After an assault in which police did not attend**:

  - Call 9-1-1 immediately for both police and medical help.
  - Get medical attention if you have been hurt.
  - Take pictures of injuries (even if the police have already done so).
  - Contact a local domestic violence program, Sexual Assault Centre, Victim Services office, or Women's Transition House for guidance, support, and information.

- **If you have children**:

  - Teach them not to get into the middle of a fight even if they want to help.
  - Teach them how to get to safety, and how to call 9-1-1.
  - Tell them who to call for help.
  - Instruct them to stay out of the kitchen as well.
  - If you have a court order against your abuser, ensure that your child's school principal, daycare, or babysitter has a copy of this order and a picture of the abuser.
  - Tell them that if they see your abuser at school, to immediately notify a teacher.

- **If you have decided to leave an abusive relationship**:

  - Have a safe place to go where the abuser cannot find you and your children, such as a trusted friend's or family member's home or women's shelter.
  - Ensure that you take the following items with you:

- ✓ birth certificates, social insurance cards, passports for you and any children
- ✓ school and medical records for you and any children
- ✓ money, bankbooks, credit cards
- ✓ keys for your home, car, office
- ✓ driver's licence and vehicle registration
- ✓ medications for you and any children
- ✓ change of clothes
- ✓ divorce/separation papers, restraining orders, peace bond papers
- ✓ copies of leases/rental agreements, house deeds
- ✓ copies of mortgage payment records, any current unpaid bills, insurance papers
- ✓ address book
- ✓ pictures, jewellery, or any other sentimental property
- ✓ child's favourite toys and blankets

• Once you have left the abusive relationship, make application for a restraining order/peace bond against the abuser.

• Make application to a court for a custody order for any children.

• Advise any friends, co-workers, or neighbours that the relationship with your abuser is now over and that if they see the abuser, or hear that you are in trouble, to call 9-1-1 immediately.

• Contact your local domestic violence centre, Sexual Assault Centre, Victim Services unit, or Women's Transition House for more information, support, and counselling referrals.

Remember that there are six important ways that you can fight domestic violence:

● Know what domestic violence is, and that it is illegal in Canada.

● Develop a safety plan as to what to do before, during, and after domestic violence has occurred.

● Call 9-1-1 for help.

● Exercise your legal rights to have the abuser held criminally and civilly responsible for his actions.

● Get the help needed for your family so that the violence will stop.

● Help other women by speaking out and educating others. Domestic violence is a crime, not a family matter.

Reporting the Crime: What to Expect

Unfortunately, no matter how well prepared a woman might be to prevent a sexual assault, the danger of this happening is still very real. As mentioned earlier, one in four Canadian women will be sexually assaulted in her lifetime. This section is intended to help women understand what to expect after an assault—from the police, the hospital, and the courts. Note that because jurisdictions around our country differ, some of the procedures described may differ slightly as well.

Good decision making is needed immediately after a sexual assault, but is extremely difficult under the stress and trauma. Not knowing what to expect and fear of unknown procedures and protocols further hamper decision making. We hope the following basic information will help. Ultimately, whatever decision you make is the right decision for you.

Police

Only 10% of women who have been sexually assaulted report the crime to police. In date or acquaintance rape, only about 1% of women report the crime. This secrecy works in favour of the sexual predator and is crucial to his ability to continue his violent crimes without being caught. By calling the police, you are beginning to take control from the predator, potentially stopping him from attacking someone else. You are holding him responsible for his criminal actions, and letting him know that he will not get away with it this time, or ever again. Reporting the crime is also an important component of healing for many women.

Sexual assault is a very serious crime and should be reported to the police as soon as possible. Unfortunately, most women are hesitant to do so for a variety of reasons, such as:

- falsely perceiving it was their fault
- expecting nothing will be done about it
- not trusting the police
- thinking no one will believe them
- fearing retaliation from the attacker

We believe that the most significant reason for most women is the fear of reprisal from their attackers. This fear is natural, especially when you consider that most attackers threaten their victims with further harm if they inform police. Reprisal does happen, but rarely. Once police are made aware of the assault, the attacker now knows that to further hurt you would be dangerous for him. If you are faced with a situation in which the attacker tells you not to call the police, you have two choices to make: say nothing to the police and live in fear; or report the crime and fight back using the justice system to your full advantage.

It is important to make this report to the police as soon as possible. Many women believe that if they do not come forward right away, they will not be believed. This is not true. Although sooner is better, reporting late is better than not reporting at all.

In most police departments, a sexual assault report is a high priority call and as such, receives immediate attention. You can report this crime either by phone or in person at the police station. In either case, you will probably speak with a uniformed police officer, who will ask for a description of the attacker and the assault. Although during this first contact the police may appear to be cold and more interested in things that seem irrelevant, all the questions are very important for the purpose of quickly apprehending the suspect. Most front line officers are highly educated in dealing with victims of sexual assault, and will be very sensitive to your needs. It is important to understand that you can have someone with you at any time during this process.

After this initial interview, the police will make arrangements for you to have a physical exam at the nearest hospital. We will talk about this physical exam in detail later in this chapter. You will not be responsible for getting yourself to the hospital, nor should you be expected to do so. The police will make all the arrangements needed to get you there in the most comfortable way possible. However, if you decide that you would rather get yourself there, then the police will respect your decision. When the examination is over, if needed, arrangements will be made by the police to get you home.

After the initial contact with the uniformed police officer, your case will be turned over to officers who specialize in these types of assaults. They will usually contact you very quickly to arrange follow-up interviews. They will ask you a variety of questions and may require you to repeat your story several times. Although this may seem to be insensitive and distrustful, remember the officers are attempting to ascertain all the facts on your behalf. Some of the questions will be very personal and may be embarrassing, such as, "Did penetration occur and if so, where?" No matter how embarrassing the questioning may become, tell the police everything that happened. Although some of the questions may seem pointless ("Was he left or right handed?", "Did he use a lubricant?", "Did he apologize for his actions?"), this detailed information may be crucial to obtaining an arrest and conviction.

When the police have finished their investigation, and if they conclude that there are reasonable and probable grounds to believe that you have been assaulted, an arrest can be made if the accused has been identified. Once this person has been arrested, he will either be held in custody or released on recognizance.

HELD IN CUSTODY

If the police believe there is a very strong likelihood that the accused may reoffend, they may hold that person in custody and place him before a provincial court judge. The judge will then decide if the accused should be remanded in custody in jail until his court date, or be released on a recognizance or bail.

RELEASED ON RECOGNIZANCE/UNDERTAKING

If the police or the courts are satisfied of the accused person's identity and believe there is little danger of the person offending again, they could release the accused on a recognizance. A recognizance is a court order with specific conditions by which the accused must abide until his court appearance date. These conditions may include no contact with you, friends or co-workers; curfews; no consumption of alcohol and/or narcotics; as well as restrictions on areas where the accused person can go (e.g. a two-block radius of where you live and work). If the person released on a recognizance breaks any of these conditions, he can be arrested immediately by police and once again placed before the courts where a judge may decide to hold the accused in custody until his court date.

Hospital

Immediately following a sexual assault, it is completely natural for you to want to take a shower or bath. By doing this, however, you are decreasing the chance that the attacker will be caught. You also should not brush your hair, brush your teeth, wash your hands, clean or brush off your clothing. The reason for this is to avoid destroying forensic evidence such as hair, saliva, blood, and semen that your attacker will have left. This evidence can be used in the event that the case goes to court.

Even if you do not intend to notify the police after being sexually assaulted, it is vitally important for your safety to still go to the hospital. Although there may be no visible signs of injury, there may be internal damage not immediately apparent. Major concerns are sexually transmitted diseases and pregnancy and tests will be conducted for these at the hospital. Follow-up visits to your doctor will still be necessary, but seeking medical aid immediately after a sexual assault is your best first step for staying healthy.

Some women who do not want police involvement are concerned that if they go to the hospital, the medical staff will contact the police. This is not true. If you do not want the police involved, the hospital will not contact them.

On arrival at the hospital, you will usually be taken to a private room, where a nurse will take information such as your name, address, medical number, and any allergies to medications. You will also be required to advise this nurse of the nature of your injuries, to which all you have to say is that you were sexually assaulted.

If it is your choice, this nurse, or the police if you have involved them, will contact the Sexual Assault Response Team (SART). This team is made up of doctors and/or nurses who have been specially trained to conduct a physical exam for sexual assault. Also on this team is a female counsellor from a local women's sexual assault centre who will be with you during and after the physical exam, if you wish. These professionals are superb at what they do, and are very sensitive to your emotional and physical needs during this difficult time.

The primary reason for this medical exam is to ensure your physical health and to deal with any medical conditions that may have resulted from the sexual assault. The SART team is also trained to carry out a forensic exam ("rape kit"), in which they collect physical evidence that can be used to positively identify your attacker through the use of DNA technology. In order to have the forensic test done, you need only agree to speak with a police officer. You are not committing yourself to a legal process, nor will charges necessarily be laid. However, the forensic information will be available should you later decide to allow the police to carry out an investigation. In some jurisdictions, a rape kit is now conducted automatically along with the physical exam (though again, you still have the choice as to whether an investigation will proceed). The remainder of our description assumes that the full physical and forensic exam is performed.

In the examination room, you will be given a hospital robe and be asked to remove the clothing that you are wearing. If the clothing was worn during the sexual assault, it will be collected, placed into paper bags, and given to the police for forensic testing. Many women are concerned that they will not have anything to wear after the exam, but most if not all hospitals have a selection of clean clothing that a woman can wear home if necessary.

The SART nurse or doctor will first ask you a series of questions about your current health and medical history, then more specific questions about your sexual behaviour and the sexual assault itself. Information that may be required includes: when you last had sexual intercourse prior to the assault; whether the attacker assaulted you vaginally, anally, or orally; whether the attacker ejaculated and if so, where; whether you scratched your attacker. These questions, although very personal, are very important, as they give the doctor or nurse a better idea of how and where injuries are most likely to be found. These questions are also very important for the purpose of collecting evidence such as semen, blood, pubic hairs, and other forensics.

The first part of the exam is usually similar to that of a yearly physical. Here the doctor or nurse is looking for general signs of injury. During this primary exam, combings of your pubic hair will be taken for the purpose of obtaining any evidence of blood, semen, and pubic hair from your attacker. If you scratched him, the nurse will take fingernail scrapings. Only the doctor and/or nurse will attend the exam, and if you wish, the sexual assault counsellor. No police officer will be present during the exam.

After this primary exam, the SART doctor and/or nurse will conduct a pelvic exam that is similar to a regular gynecological exam. You will be asked to lie down on an examination table with your feet placed in metal footrests, so that your knees are bent and legs are apart. The SART doctor or nurse then examines the outside of the vagina and anus looking for any cuts, bruises, or traces of semen outside of these areas. After inserting a warmed speculum into your vagina, the doctor or nurse looks for sperm and other signs of recent intercourse such as a torn hymen or vaginal or rectal inflammations. Swabs and flushings are taken for the purpose of collecting any semen that might still be present. The doctor or nurse may also take evidence from your mouth or rectum depending upon how you were sexually assaulted. Two more physical exams check for injury by means of a second vaginal exam and a rectal exam. In the vaginal exam, the doctor places two fingers in your vagina with one hand, while gently palpating the lower abdomen. In the rectal exam, the doctor or nurse briefly checks the rectum with a finger. After this there will be routine collections of urine and blood samples. Finally, the doctor and/or nurse will discuss with you other important issues such as sexually transmitted diseases and pregnancy.

When the hospital exam is over, the doctor or nurse will hand over all of the forensic evidence collected to the police. Arrangements will be made to have you taken home, and if you wish, to have someone with you. The counsellor from the sexual assault centre will usually stay in contact with you, and will provide you with phone numbers of people you can talk to during your recovery process.

Court

After police have collected the evidence, conducted their investigation, and arrested a suspect, they then prepare a "report to Crown Counsel." This report contains all relevant evidence and can include your statement, documentation of forensic evidence, a statement from the examining doctor or nurse, a statement from the suspect, and any other information that the police believe is important. This report is then reviewed by the Crown prosecutor. In a criminal trial the Crown prosecutor presents the case on behalf of the state, i.e., Canada, and not you personally. In a criminal proceeding, you are considered a witness for the Crown.

The Crown prosecutor then makes a decision as to whether there is enough evidence to proceed in a criminal trial. If she feels that there is not enough evidence to proceed, she will advise the police, and if there is no more evidence that can be brought forward, there will be no criminal prosecution. If a case is rejected by the Crown, it does *not* mean that no one believes your story. Rather, the Crown understands what an ordeal the court process can be and will avoid needlessly subjecting a rape victim to the process, if there is no chance of a conviction. This is why it is so important that you be as thorough and forthcoming as you can with the police during their investigation, even if what you have to say is embarrassing or might, in your opinion, damage your credibility.

If the Crown decides that there is enough evidence to proceed, the suspect will be formally charged and a court date will be set for either a preliminary hearing or a trial. At the preliminary hearing a judge decides if there is enough evidence, in the eyes of the court, to go on to a criminal trial. If there is insufficient evidence, the case will be dismissed. Otherwise, a court date will be set. The accused party can decide if he wishes to be tried by judge alone or by judge and jury. It can take months to finally get to trial.

Once the case finally gets to court, you will be expected to testify as a witness for the Crown. This process is probably the most feared by women, because here they have to relive the entire experience all over again in front of a courtroom that may be packed with strangers. The Crown is sensitive to this, and will offer to guide you through the court process. A number of Victim Services groups also work closely with sexual assault survivors, and help them prepare for court.

Once you have finished your testimony for the Crown, the lawyer representing your attacker has the opportunity to cross-examine you. The job of the defence lawyer is to obtain a not guilty verdict and he will try everything legally possible to achieve this goal. Unfortunately, Canada, unlike the United States, does not have a rape shield law. This law protects victims of sexual assault from having defence lawyers attack their past sexual history or character. In Canada, if the defence lawyer argues successfully that your past sexual history or character is relevant to the case, then the court will allow this line of questioning to take place. Many women fear being publicly discredited in this way. The predator hopes that this fact alone will prevent you from giving evidence against him in court.

Do not allow him to control you—take back that control. To help survive the ordeal, focus on the fact that what he did was criminal. This is your chance to make him pay for what he has done to you and hopefully prevent him from doing the same thing to other women.

After the cross-examination, the Crown may ask you further questions to clarify information you gave to the defence. After this you will be excused by the judge and if you wish you may stay to hear the rest of the evidence. At the conclusion of the Crown's case, the defence may call witnesses, including his client, to attempt to disprove facts made by Crown. Final arguments are then made to the court, in which both the Crown and defence will again go over the evidence and possibly argue over specific legal precedents. After the final arguments, the judge and/or jury will review all the evidence provided and make a judgement.

In Canada, a guilty verdict requires a person to be guilty beyond a reasonable doubt. If the defence can prove any reasonable doubt about what took place, then the court must find in favour of the accused and find him not guilty of the offence. If the accused is found guilty, then the court decides the punishment. This can vary depending upon a number of factors, including past criminal history and the nature and seriousness of the crime. There is a real possibility that even if found guilty, your attacker may not have to go to jail. This may be very hard for a survivor to understand, but that is the way our judicial system currently operates.

After the criminal process is over, you may also wish to consider filing a civil suit against your attacker. The civil process differs from the criminal one in that you have to hire a lawyer to represent your case. In a civil trial, you become the plaintiff while your attacker becomes the defendant. In a civil trial, the burden of proof is less than that in a criminal trial. In a civil proceeding, guilt is determined on a "balance of probabilities" rather than on the "beyond a reasonable doubt" basis. The purpose of a civil suit is usually to obtain financial compensation for the pain and suffering that you have endured as a result of the attack. While you could never really be "compensated" for your ordeal, at least you are given the satisfaction of knowing that the attacker has to pay in some manner for what he has done. There is also public acknowledgement of the wrong that was done to you.

Discuss your options with trusted friends and with advisors knowledgeable about the procedures involved. We hope that if you are ever faced with the decision to report a sexual assault you will do so. Remember, though, that the decision is yours alone to make, and whatever it is, it will be the right one for you at that time.

The Recovery Process

Healing vs. Recovery

Can a survivor truly "heal" after being sexually assaulted? The answer depends on your interpretation of the word. Webster's defines *heal* as "to make or become healthy, sound, or whole, to cure." If you break a bone, you go to a doctor and have it fixed. Over time, your bone is "made whole" and healthy and the injury often can't be seen or felt. We don't believe that a survivor of a sexual assault can really heal from the experience in this fashion, but we do believe that she can recover from it. The recovery process is more like a cut that leaves a scar—it is still always with the survivor to some degree. The use of the word "heal" presents the survivor with the misleading belief that she will someday be able to put what happened totally behind her. A more realistic recovery process is one in which the survivor understands that she has had a traumatic experience that will stay with her for the rest of her life, but one which need not control her for the rest of her life.

As a survivor, it is important that you take steps towards regaining control of your life. At first, picking up the pieces of your life may seem more difficult than you can handle. Even though you may want to forget that this horrible experience ever took place, it has now become a part of you. Yet, how you deal with the aftermath of the assault will have a direct impact on your future well-being as a survivor, not a victim. You will need support, understanding, and love from family and close friends, and may benefit from professional counselling.

Rape Trauma Syndrome

As a victim (we like to use the term survivor) of a sexual assault, you may experience strong physical, emotional, and cognitive reactions to the trauma. The Rape Trauma Syndrome is identified by similar symptoms and behaviours exhibited by many survivors of sexual assault. Although some survivors may not experience this Syndrome, an awareness of its symptoms may help those women who do. Your reactions may be different from those that we list, or you may experience one or two and not all of them. Also, the intensity and duration of the Syndrome will vary from person to person, but may last for months or even years.

Generally, the symptoms occur in three phases, although some symptoms may overlap or reoccur. The time span for each phase varies widely, depending on the person, although the first phase often characterizes the first day or so after the assault.

PHASE ONE: CONFUSION

- confusion, shock
- disbelief or denial that assault happened
- intense mood swings
- fear of what others will think
- fear of the attacker
- shaking, cold sweats, nausea
- overreaction to noise
- loss of appetite
- sleeplessness
- nightmares
- loss of normal energy level
- loss of short-term memory
- sense of loss, violation
- feelings of shame or humiliation
- self-blame

PHASE TWO: TRYING TO REORGANIZE

In this phase, many survivors will reorganize their daily routines in an attempt to regain control of their situation. Some common behaviours and symptoms at this time include:

- fear of the environment or of people who remind the survivor of the assault
- changing daily routines or moving from a residence if the assault took place there
- ending relationships with boyfriend, husband, girlfriend, family members
- immediately beginning a new relationship
- distrust of others
- change in sleeping patterns
- continued loss of normal energy levels
- weight loss or gain
- feelings of intense anger and rage

- depression
- withdrawal from sexual activity
- wanting to change personal appearance
- continued mood swings
- continued self-blame
- self-medication with alcohol and/or drugs

PHASE THREE: INTEGRATION

At this point, the survivor has integrated her feelings and reactions to the assault while taking control of her daily life. Some of the above-noted reactions may still remain, but if the survivor has received proper counselling, the assault is no longer the only thing on her mind. In this last phase of recovery, the trauma no longer dominates her life and things return to a reasonable state of normalcy. The survivor is able to express and resolve her feelings of fear and rage about the assault, and be able to blame the person who attacked her instead of blaming herself. To get to this final phase of recovery is not easy, and will be reached at varying times by different people. To help speed this process, we strongly recommend that all survivors of sexual assault seek professional guidance.

Getting Professional Help

Will every survivor of a sexual assault need professional counselling? Not necessarily. However, a good sexual assault counsellor will help you understand what you are going through during the recovery process, and that what you are experiencing during your recovery is normal. The guidance of a skilled counsellor will be especially needed for those whose family, close friends, and lovers are unable to come to terms with the sexual assault and emotional distress.

Sexual assault crisis counsellors have a unique understanding of the physical and emotional reactions that you will be experiencing and will help guide you through the recovery process. The goal of a rape crisis counsellor is to help the survivor learn to take positive control over her life once again.

The best way to find a person who specializes in counselling sexual assault survivors is to ask for information at your local Sexual Assault Centre. You may also wish to ask your family doctor for referrals. If you are at all uncomfortable with your counsellor, go elsewhere. This person will have a direct effect on your recovery process.

Remember:

- It is natural for you to feel upset during the recovery process.
- Try not to feel guilty or blame yourself for the assault. Guilt lies with the attacker and not you.
- It is important to share your feelings with a professional counsellor or someone you trust.
- Be patient with yourself; the recovery process will take time.

Being a Friend

If a friend discloses to you that she has been sexually assaulted:

LISTEN, BUT DO NOT JUDGE

The most important thing you can do is to be a willing and sympathetic listener. Be available as much as you can. It is very important that you accept her version of what took place and be supportive. If you have feelings about what happened (e.g. that she showed poor judgement in the situation), deal with them separately. Keep what she says confidential.

OFFER SHELTER

If it is at all possible, stay with your friend at her place or let her spend at least one night at yours. She needs a place to feel safe. This is not the time for a sexual assault survivor to be alone, especially if the assault took place in her home.

GIVE HER COMFORT

Your friend has been violated in the worst way possible and needs to be comforted and nurtured.

LET HER KNOW THAT SHE IS NOT TO BLAME

Many survivors will blame themselves for what has taken place. Your friend needs to know that the rapist is to blame and not her.

BE PATIENT AND UNDERSTANDING

Do not place a timetable on your friend as to when you feel that she should be over this traumatic experience. Every survivor has her own rate of recovery. Be willing to listen long after the assault has taken place.

ENCOURAGE ACTION

Encourage your friend to go to the hospital, and to call the police and the local sexual assault centre. Let her know that she can go to the hospital and seek counselling without police involvement, if she prefers. Whatever your friend's choice, respect her decision.

DO NOT BE OVERLY PROTECTIVE

An important part of the recovery process is to encourage a survivor to take control of her life by making her own decisions. If you make decisions for her, you take away some of her power, and power is exactly what she needs. Even if you disagree with the choices your friend is making, accept them. It is much more important for your friend to make decisions and to have them respected, than it is for you to impose what you think is right.

HELP HER TO TAKE CARE OF HERSELF

Often, trauma victims neglect the basics necessary for physical and emotional health. It is vital to the recovery process and her well-being that she gets enough sleep, proper nutrition, and regular exercise.

CHAPTER SIX

Fear As Your Ally

A recent study conducted by the Model Mugging organization in the United States determined that in 80% of attacks on women, the predator frightened his victim into submission simply by using verbal intimidation. The mind guides the body. The predator knows that if he is able to paralyze your mind through fear, your body will freeze also, no matter how much physical training you have.

What is fear? Most people view fear as an extremely negative feeling which causes one to totally freeze and panic, and as a result get hurt. Although this is a common belief, it is not quite accurate.

Fear is both a physical and an emotional response to a perceived threat or danger. The physical reactions prepare us to confront and survive a dangerous situation, by readying autonomic functions for self-defence and trauma. Heart rate increases; adrenaline and blood-clotting enzymes are released to make the body stronger, faster and less likely to feel pain. Hearing and vision become more acute. The emotional response differs from person to person, based upon training and learned past experiences. What may seem to be a threatening situation to one person may not be to another.

This emotional response to fear is both learned and voluntary. A learned experience is generally taught to you. For instance, if you are a parent who has arachnophopia, and you see a spider crawling across the floor, your first reaction may be to scream and jump up on a chair. Your small child will soon begin to react to spiders in the same way. Seeing the spider will trigger the learned fear response.

The voluntary reaction is what we choose to do when faced with a dangerous situation. Unfortunately, many women and men use fear in a self-defeating, negative way rather than with a challenging positive attitude.

Perceived threats trigger our learned and voluntary responses and any of three will occur: flight, fight, or hypervigilance. Allowing yourself to become stuck in a state of hypervigilance, which is freezing in place both mentally and physically, will most certainly allow an attacker to succeed, or will prevent you from being proactive and dealing with the situation.

The emotional response need not be mental immobility; it can be trained and utilized as a voluntary, positive force. An analogy can be drawn by comparing the fear emotion with electricity. When used positively and appropriately, electricity runs our lives; when used negatively and carelessly, electricity can kill. What you choose to do with the emotion of fear—allow it to control you, or harness the energy—is up to you, but the decision could save your life.

How do you choose the flight or fight response and not the hypervigilance response? The answer is simple in concept; ask yourself: "Am I *threatened* or am I *challenged?*"

To better understand this, place yourself in the following scenario: You are in an office building that has thirty floors, and wanting to go to the top floor, you decide to use the elevator. When the elevator arrives, with no one inside, you enter and start your ascent. Arriving at the tenth floor, the door opens and standing in front of you is an unknown male, 6'5", 250 pounds, built like a Mac truck, brandishing a knife and saying, "Shut up and I won't hurt you—if you scream, you're dead." Now ask yourself, "Am I threatened or am I challenged?" Most people, when faced with this situation, will say they are threatened.

The brain makes a decision for the future based upon past experience and training; it guides the body. No matter how much physical training you have to deal with an attacker who is about to assault you, if you stay in the "threatened" mindset, you will go into hypervigilance mode, come to a paralytic standstill, and be at the mercy of the attacker. You need to get "challenged."

How do you get from "threatened" to "challenged"? By consciously saying the word "BUT." In the elevator, when the door opens and you are faced with the attacker armed with the knife, what should be going through your mind is, "I'm in a bad situation, BUT if he takes another step, I will do...."

The powerful word "but" challenges the brain and allows it to work. It can now find answers to the questions it is being faced with, such as, "How am I going to get out of this situation as quickly and safely as possible?" Once the brain is allowed to work, the physical training and experience you may have can be applied. In other words, instead of freezing into a complete standstill, you begin to take some action to protect yourself.

A good self-defence course with realistic scenerios is beneficial not only in teaching you physical strategies, but in helping you realize that you *can* use fear to your advantage. However, even if you do not have the self-defence training or life experience to deal with a specific threat, the "challenged" brain will begin to adapt, overcome, and improvise to find a way for you to stay safe. There are hundreds of instances in which women with no prior self-defence training have physically resisted their attackers and survived. They challenged themselves.

As previously stated, in 80% of attacks on women, the predator used only verbal intimidation to scare his victim into a submissive state of hypervigilance. To overcome this, you must allow the brain to work, challenge it to mentally figure a way out of the dangerous situation, and to physically release the body energy that fear stimulates. Decide to focus and direct the mental and physical forces into a powerful attack of your own, and allow the full impact of the fear response to propel your mind, body, and soul against the attacker. Fear can be your greatest ally in a dangerous situation, but it can also be your worst enemy. The choice is ultimately yours.

Selected Bibliography and Resources

BOOKS, REPORTS, AND ARTICLES

Association of American Colleges. 1987. *Friends Raping Friends: Could It Happen to You?* Washington DC.

Brickman, Julie and John Briere. 1984. Incidence of Rape and Sexual Assault in an Urban Canadian Population. *International Journal of Women's Studies* 7(3): 195-207.

Burrese, Alain. 1996. *Hard-Won Wisdom from the School of Hard Knocks: How to Avoid a Fight and Things to Do When You Can't or Don't Want To.* Boulder, CO: Paladin Press.

Christensen, Loren. 1996. *How to Live Safely in a Dangerous World.* Miami: Action Direct Incorporated.

DeBecker, Gavin. 1998. *The Gift of Fear.* New York: Dell Publishing.

Justice Institute Of British Columbia. 1993. *Sexual Assault Victim Services Workers Handbook.* Vancouver, BC.

Leung, Debbie. 1991. *Self Defense: The Womanly Art of Self-Care, Intuition and Choice.* Tacoma, WA: R and M Press.

Lipman, Ira. 1997. *How to Protect Yourself from Crime.* New York: The Reader's Digest Association Incorporated.

MacYoung, Marc and Chris Pfouts. 1994. *Safe in the City: A Streetwise Guide to Avoid Being Robbed, Raped, Ripped Off, or Run Over.* Boulder, CO: Paladin Press.

Matsakis, Aphrodite. 1996. *I Can't Over It: A Handbook for Trauma Survivors.* 2nd edition. Oakland, CA: New Harbinger Publications.

Metro Action Committee on Public Violence Against Women and Children. 1992. *Moving Forward: Canadian Urban Victimization Survey.* Toronto, ON.

Ministry of Women's Equality. 1992. *Is Anyone Listening? Report Of The British Columbia Task Force On Family Violence.* Victoria, BC.

Mizell, Louis Jr. 1993. *Street Sense for Women.* New York: Berkley Publishing Group.

Ontario Women's Directorate. 1990. *Sexual Assault: Dispelling the Myths.* Ottawa, ON.

Pettifer, Shirley and Janet Torge. 1997. *Sexual Assault.* Revised edition. Montreal, QC: Montreal Health Press.

Policing Services Program. 1997. *Canadian Crime Statistics.* Ottawa, ON: Canadian Centre for Justice Statistics, Statistics Canada.

Pottie Bunge, Valerie and Andrea Levett. 1998. *Family Violence in Canada: A Statistical Profile.* Ottawa, ON: Canadian Centre for Justice Statistics, Statistics Canada.

Rafkin, Louse. 1995. *Street Smarts: A Personal Safety Guide for Women.* New York: HarperCollins.

Snortland, Ellen. 1998. *Beauty Bites Beast: Awakening the Warrior within Women and Girls.* Pasadena, CA: Trilogy Books.

Thomas, Matt, Denise Loveday, and Larry Strauss. 1995. *Defend Yourself: Every Woman's Guide to Safe-Guarding Her Life.* New York: Avon Books.

Thompson, Geoff. 1997. *Dead or Alive, The Choice is Yours: The Definitive Self-Protection Handbook.* Boulder, CO: Paladin Press.

Various articles, *British Columbia Crime Prevention Association News Magazine* and *Blue Line Magazine.*

WEBSITES

Arming Women Against Rape and Endangerment (AWARE)
http://www.aware.org/index.html

Assault Prevention Information Network
http://ccwf.cc.utexas.edu/~weiss/

British Columbia Ministry of Women's Equality [and links]
http://www.weq.gov.bc.ca

Canadian Bankers Association [electronic banking, safe shopping on-line]
http://www.cba.ca/eng/Statistics/FastFacts/abms.htm
http://www.cba.ca/eng/Tools/Brochures/tools_commerce.htm

Federal Trade Commission (FTC) [much useful information on E-Commerce and the Internet, including the latest scams]
http://www.ftc.gov/bcp/menu-internet.htm

National Crime Prevention Council (of Canada) [with extensive directory of Canadian crime prevention organizations] http://www.crime-prevention.org/

"The Police Notebook" Internet Safety Page, University of Oklahoma Department of Public Safety [and links] http://www.ou.edu/oupd/inetmenu.htm

Sexual Assault Information Page http://www.cs.utk.edu/~bartley/saInfoPage.html

Statistics Canada http://www.statcan.ca/english

Web Psychos, Stalkers, and Pranksters: How to Protect Yourself in Cyberspace [site based on the book by Michael Banks; updated frequently by the author] http://w3.one.net/~banks/psycho.htm

ORGANIZATIONS

Canadians Against Violence Everywhere Advocating Its Termination (C.A.V.E.A.T.), Suite 3 - 164, 3350 Fairview Street, Burlington, ON L7N 3L5
Phone: (905) 632-1733 Fax: (905) 632-3039
E-mail: info@caveat.org

National Crime Prevention Council [contact for extensive directory of national, provincial, and local Canadian crime prevention organizations], 8 – 130 Albert Street, Ottawa, ON K1A 0H8 Phone: (613) 957-4640 Fax: (613) 952-3515
E-mail: ncpc@web.net or website listed above

Personal Protection Systems (Darren and Beth Laur's company) [safety awareness seminars and physical self-defence training for all levels], 654 Hoy Lake Road, Victoria, BC V9B 3P7
Phone and Fax: (250) 478-9119
E-mail: eightball@pacificcoast.net

Rape Aggression Defense (R.A.D.) [self-defence training for women offered through most universities]
R.A.D. CANADA, 3915 - 150th Street, Edmonton, AB T6R 1J5
(403) 448-2825

Victim Services Organizations—contact through your local police department